Gine

ZERO

Translated by Rosie Hedger

nordisk books

Published by Nordisk Books, 2018
www.nordiskbooks.com

Translated from *Null*, copyright © 2013, Forlaget Oktober AS
Published by Agreement with Oslo Literary Agency.

This translation has been published with the financial support of NORLA

NORLA
NORWEGIAN LITERATURE ABROAD

Printed and bound in Great Britain by Clays Ltd, Elcograf S.p.A.

A CIP catalogue record for this book is
available from the British Library

ISBN 9780995485235

Gine Cornelia Pedersen

ZERO

Translated by Rosie Hedger

Also by Nordisk Books

Havoc
Tom Kristensen

You can't betray your best friend and learn to sing at the same time
Kim Hiorthøy

Love/War
Ebba Witt-Brattström

0

I'm 10 years old
I absorb everything unfiltered
I think that God is listening when I pray
I've seen three dead bodies, two old and one young
I cry at night and feel as if I'm all alone and no one can save me
I feel sorry for Mum and Dad
I realise that the concept of home has never truly existed
I think about the fact that when I grow up and I'm allowed to decide things for myself, my joy will be complete
I feel certain I'm going to live forever, but I think about death almost every day
I root for the villains in every Disney film, but I don't let on to anyone
I do the kind of things to my sister that suggest I've got hidden sociopathic traits
I think that one hundred kroner is a fortune

I've only ever smoked two cigarettes
I've got a newborn baby brother
I pick up a piece of gravel and scratch a car
I've kissed five boys
I'm going to be an actor or an artist when I grow up
I've got three imaginary friends
I play with Barbie when nobody's looking
I can cycle a long, long way without getting tired
I believe in everlasting love
I think Pamela Anderson is pretty

Life is going to be good
One day everything is going to be good
One day
When I grow up
Everything is going to be good
I'll stand on stage
There'll be a spotlight on me and me alone
It'll be clear for everyone to see that I'm beautiful and talented and brilliant at everything that I do
I'll win a prize
I have to win a prize
I cry watching the Oscars
I leaf through trashy magazines at Granny's house
Cut out pictures of pretty ladies and men with nice hair and slim bodies and stick them into notepads
I end up with ten notepads' worth of clippings
I stand in front of the mirror for hours every day and practise my look of delight when they announce that I've won
Practise having my picture taken
I make a speech:
'Thank you! Thank you all. But there's one very special person I'd particularly like to thank. I couldn't have done this without you, my darling husband, Leonardo DiCaprio! I love you! I always will!'
I have grapefruit for breakfast
It's what Cindy Crawford eats when she wants to lose weight, she says

Eating grapefruit for breakfast is fun even though it
tastes horrible
I'm influenced by absolutely everything around me
I need to be entertained
There's a fire inside me
I wonder when anyone else will realise that there's a fire
inside me
I've got so much to offer
Nobody has any idea how much I've got to offer
It's just a question of time before I'm discovered, I
think to myself
I want a nose piercing
I force the needle point of a compass through my
nostril and stick a safety pin through the hole
Dad goes mad when he sees it
I take the safety pin out
I smudge black makeup around my eyes
I start to feel angry
I wonder when anyone will realise just how angry I am
I'm angry
I read about Satan
Scribble his name on every last page of my school
planner
All hail Satan
In Satan We Trust
I feel embarrassed that I once bothered cutting out
pictures of celebrities from trashy magazines, that I
managed to fill ten whole notepads with them

I burn them in a ritual for my eyes only
It's meant to represent the start of a new era
I've no idea what that new era might bring
Really it just marks the end of the previous one
God knows what's to come
Or maybe it's Satan who knows?
It's a hard pill to swallow when I realise that the picture
of Leonardo on my bedside table has to go
It feels all wrong
He's the only one who really understands me
I'll never forget him
I'll bury my dreams of our life together
Bury them along with dreams of my day in the sun
Bury them way down deep in a bottomless grave
I feel angry
Always, always angry
I don't understand how anything works
I've no idea what's going on or how things could ever
change
Something tingles inside me
I'm so bored
Something tingles inside me and all I can see outside
my window is fields
All I can hear is the buzzing of a fly as it attempts to
escape through a closed window
I'm forever waiting for my dinner, waiting for school
SCHOOL
I've been left all alone

I yearn for my dad
I remember the time he let me and my sister sit on his back while he pretended to be a horse
He crawled around on his knees, whinnying
It was amazing
I'll never forget it
I got him to drink from a bowl of water and eat an apple and a carrot
Dad will always be a hero to me
Dad wears a denim jacket and smokes Lucky Strikes and drives an old, red rust bucket of a car
He comes to pick us up at weekends
Every other weekend
We watch TV and eat pizza
I want to go with him to Oslo
I want to go home to Oslo
Oslo is paradise
Oslo is the place where everything thrives and nothing is boring and there are no fields to be seen
Just lawns and parks and asphalt
I love Oslo
Oslo is life
I can't breathe here
I crave some kind of sound or smell
Something interesting
Anything at all
The smell of a pavement café
The smell of asphalt in the baking hot sun

The smell of saltwater
The sound of a tram going by
The sound of sirens
The sound of a weird, drunken stranger shouting at the top of his lungs
Nobody shouts out here
Nobody is weird
WHY AM I HERE
I'm so bored that I start drinking vodka
I mix it with different soft drinks
I make a bong from an old bottle and start smoking weed
Start cutting my arms
I'm just an average angry, tormented teenager
A classic case
I cry when I'm drunk
Vomit
And cry
And kiss anyone who's up for it
I've got breasts now
They're bigger than all the other girls'
I bind my chest to make them flat
I want to be flat, to be skinny
Don't want a single scrap of spare fat on me
I just want everything to be cool
I always miss the mark when it comes to friends
The selection is inadequate
Or maybe it's me who's inadequate

I can't rule that out
It's the thought that occurs to me most often, actually
The thought that always comes to mind
When I finally escape this dump, I'll burn the entire
fucking village to the ground
The village and everyone in it
Everyone apart from Grandma and Grandad and my
cousins, anyway
I'll spare most of my family, but everyone else can just
die already
I can't be bothered caring about anything that happens
at home
Mum can go to hell
She can take her stupid new boyfriend and his ugly
accent with her
And my stupid brother who can't talk and does nothing
but eat and babble away
And my stupid sister who keeps her bedroom tidy and
saves up all her pocket money
She must have more than a thousand kroner stashed
away in a jar
I help myself when I want to buy cigarettes
I can't be bothered caring about anything
I don't care
About anything
And even though I feel guilty all of the time, it's not
enough to make me do anything about it
And that makes me hate myself all the more

It makes me stifle the tiny bit of integrity that's left
And that makes me do things that make me feel guilty,
things that I stifle again, and so on and so forth
I've built some sort of wall
I've made some sort of decision
I've got hope
And that hope is Oslo
When I make it to Oslo, I'll be better
I'll unleash everything inside me that's constructive and
good
I'll get a job and pay my sister back every krone I ever
borrowed from her
I'll chase my dreams
Dare to be myself again, to be happy and strange
But until I make it there, until I make it to Oslo?
Standstill

1

I'm 16 years old
I've persuaded Mum to let me move out for college
I feel happy and uninhibited
Unburdened by any core
I've got a summer job in a waterpark
The uniform is ridiculous, yellow and blue with a
    baseball cap
I refuse to wear the cap
My boss tells me it's the cap or the job
I make 60 kroner per hour
Sell ice creams as I'm forced to watch paedos in
    speedos pass me by
To listen as brats from Bergen beg their mothers for ice
    creams and hot dogs in thick, western drawls
I pocket cash from the till to compensate for the
    unreasonable working conditions
Fistfuls of the stuff
Feel like Robin Hood
Shove the notes inside my bra and shoes

Thousands of kroner
Spend my spoils on weed and beer and soft drinks and CDs and bus tickets
Ignore the phone when my boyfriend calls
I catch the bus to Tønsberg to see a friend
Meet others there who smoke weed too
Can't ever get high enough
Smoke everyone else under the table
Take the bus a few more stops and smoke some more
I've decided I don't give a shit about anything, I'm just going to do whatever I want
I break up with my boyfriend
We've been together for two years and he thinks it's time to propose
I think he needs his head checked
He loses it and slams the dashboard
I tell him I'm too young to settle down, that it's time we went our separate ways
He doubles over at the wheel
I ask him what's wrong
He grabs my wrist and tells me I can't leave him
Says he can't live without me
Says it's probably best we end things here and now, together
Once and for all
I tell him I'm still young, that it would be stupid to throw in the towel now
I turn to grab the door handle

He clutches at my wrist
Won't let go
Holds me tighter, pulls me closer
I tell him he needs to let me go
He starts the engine
I ask him what he thinks he's doing, keep my cool, ask him to let me out
He locks the door
He's gazing into the distance, one hand around my wrist and the other on the wheel
Steering us towards the main road
We're hurtling along at 90 miles per hour
I start thinking about the most trivial things
Like the fact there are only two cigarettes left in my pack, that I need to pick up some more before the shop closes
That I need to shower before bed tonight
That I'll make a couple of sandwiches when I get home
I'm going to die
I grab my phone to call Mum
He snatches it from my hand and tosses it out of the window
I beg for my life
Scream that I love him, that I want to spend the rest of my life with him
He tells me that's exactly what's going to happen
I realise it's too late
Can't hear a thing above the roar of the engine

We drive past a friend's house
The kitchen light is on
I can see the dining table and someone at the sink
I think of Mum
I scream
This must be it, my final death cry
The most primitive of sounds
The origin of everything
The end of everything
Soon there will be nothing
No sounds, no thoughts
I can't believe my last breath will be scented with Little
    Trees air freshener
I realise that death is a surreal affair
I prepare myself
Let go
He screams too
I see the rock face
Bury my face in my hands

5 years old on a beach in Brazil
8 years old at a tragic funeral
10 years old on a police horse for my birthday
14 years old and losing my virginity in a field

He slams on the brakes
The car spins
It comes to a halt

My hands are still covering my face
I look over at him
He's just sitting there
He reverses, turns the car around
Drives slowly back in the direction we came from
Lights a cigarette
I start laughing
He says sorry, that he hadn't meant to lose it like that
I laugh
Loud and frenzied
It hurts my stomach
It freaks him out seeing me laugh like that, he says
But the whole thing is hysterical
All I can do is laugh
He pulls up outside my building
Tells me he's going to kill himself
That this will be the last I see of him
I'm laughing uncontrollably
He rocks back and forth
I stop laughing
Take the keys from him
Tell him he mustn't kill himself, that he can come inside
with me
He can't walk, he says
I have to help him inside
He curls up in the foetal position on my bed
I lie down on the floor
Ask him if he's OK

'Monster,' he says
He repeats the word over and over for an hour, rocking back and forth
His fists are clenched
I feel sorry for him
Eventually he stops his rocking and muttering
He leaves without a word
I tear off the bedsheets
Cut them to pieces
Life isn't logical
Life isn't
Fuck, this isn't
I make up my mind to remove this
It's going
Someone else can have it
I don't want it
I don't want it

I've fallen in love with my childhood friend, Jorg
I've made up my mind that this summer is going to be
good
I smoke weed morning, noon and night
I've taught Jorg to roll a joint, to crave the high
I've taught him to kiss and to fuck
I'm so madly in love that I can't even stand up
It's physically painful
It's hot outside
But we don't care about the weather
We hole up in his boyhood bedroom
His bed was built with twelve-year-olds in mind
We sleep as one
Sweat as one
Breathe as one
Laugh as one
Watch the world go by together and smoke as one
Sometimes I feel like someone is watching us through
his window at night
We draw the curtains
Sometimes I hyperventilate in his lap
He just lays his hands on my head
Then we watch a comedy
Or some Japanese anime
Roll up what's left of the butts in the ashtray
Buy crap, dry weed and cheap cola and white bread
We laugh about the fact that we're fucked
We like things that way

He reads good books
We talk about them
He's smarter than I am
I read books he likes to try to get closer to his way of thinking
I dye my hair darker
We're so close that I want to feed off him
It's not enough having him inside me during sex, I want to be absorbed by him
I want in
I cry when I realise it can never be
We start college, we're in the same class
I spend more and more of my time in tears
Dye my hair darker
We spend our Friday nights watching game shows
We laugh when it hits us what losers we are
He wraps his arms around me
I'm just as sad whether his arms are around me or not
Everyone else in our class is a moron
I'm so proud that Jorg is mine
We scream and shout about how unhappy we are
The others back off because we spend too much of our time complaining
We laugh and complain louder than ever
I feel angry about the fact that he's smarter than I am
I wish that I were smart
Wish that I were an autist

That I had some kind of talent that was mine and mine alone, a talent that justified my existence
The girls in the year above pounce on me
They single me out as victim number one in their end-of-year revelries
Hunt me down during breaktimes
Jorg tells me to ignore them
Some scumbag beats him up for wearing a beanie and smoking weed
I'm scared
I'm staying with Jorg and his dad
We live up in the attic
His bed gets narrower and narrower
I come out in a rash all over my face and body
Scratch myself to the point of bleeding
The wounds become infected
Yellow liquid oozes from my face
The doctor tells me I need to relax
I cry every night
We both cry together
Cry about the fact that we're surrounded by idiots and there's no place for us
I long to be accepted by the idiots
Long to be put first, to be valued
I daydream about life at the centre of the action
Picture everyone applauding me
Laughing at my jokes
I lighten my hair and sign up for the end-of-term show

I embarrass myself
Walk around more hunched over than ever before
I hide around corners smoking weed and steal from the shops around town
I fail my exam
Fail all of my assessments
I'm bored
I skip class whenever I get the chance
I have weird sexual fantasies about my male teachers
I have weird sexual fantasies about lots of people
I go the nurse's office during class to avoid sitting at my desk feeling pissed off at the blonde heads up by the teacher's desk, arms waving back and forth as if their lives depended on it
Then college is over
Done
When it comes time to write memories in each other's yearbooks, nobody writes anything about me
I have to come up with my own suggestion for the girls in the class to use if they want to
They tell me it's all the same to them
I want to break up with Jorg
I can't face living as one anymore
I can't face having so much to lose anymore
He doesn't understand, he says, he thought ours was an alliance
I leave

Take my clothes from the wardrobe in his childhood
bedroom
I've fallen in love with one of the girls in my year
She's not a lesbian, she tells me
I tell her that she is, that I can tell that sort of thing
about people
Then we're together, just like that
Somewhere inside me, Jorg is all I want
I have no core
I take what I need from others less hollow than I am
Jorg makes me feel as if I have a core of my own
That's probably why I want him to hate me so much

2

It's autumn
I've moved to Oslo
Finally, I've moved to Oslo
This is it, I think to myself, this is when life begins
Everything is going to be good
I work in a nursing home cleaning up shit up every day
One of the patients smears his shit everywhere in his sleep
It's green
It has a stench like death
I know I'm supposed to feel sorry for him and to help him to clean it up
I find the whole thing repulsive
Throw up in the sink
The man sings
He sings rude songs
Songs filled with words I didn't know old people even knew
The whole thing is absurd

The shit just oozes out of him
It's never-ending
I write in my report that he never stops shitting, that he doesn't understand that he shouldn't eat it or smear it everywhere
They tell me they're well aware, that he'll never learn
This is it for me, every day
Every day spent with people who are waiting for death

I start a new job at a nursery school
We have to take the kids out even though it's bitter outside
It's freezing cold
I just want to curl up in one of the wagons we cart the kids around in
I feel myself getting annoyed at the children, well-fed and comfortable and wrapped up in warm blankets
I want those things for me
I want to go to sleep
I can't be arsed with any of this
I quit
I get a job in a fashionable clothing store
Everyone there dresses the same
Like a cross between punks and business management students
I just wear any old thing
The manager tells me I need to wear something they sell there

I tell her there was nothing in the contract about a uniform
She laughs, thinks I'm joking
Pulls out a pair of Levis and a t-shirt: Dare to be different, Diesel gives you the fuel to break out
She grabs me a stupid hat and a Palestinian scarf
I look ridiculous, feel a lump in my throat whenever I catch sight of myself in the mirror
When customers come into the shop, she says: 'Hey, how's it going?'
I feel embarrassed, look at them apologetically
She turns around, tells me it's my turn now, I need to say hello
'Hi,' I say
She doesn't look happy
Says it's no good me being so quiet
I burst into tears when I get home
Tell my girlfriend I want to quit
She tells me it's just how things are when you're starting out somewhere new, that I'll get used to it before long
I tell her it feels like I'm selling myself

There's a work party on Friday night
They have their own club
A tiny cellar on Karl Johans gate
There's a guy there doing a live radio show
Another guy slaps him with a fish

I have no idea what's going on
Everybody around me is laughing and bumping into
me
There are lots of Swedes in the crowd
'Snygt,' they murmur in approval, *'grymt.'*
I pretend to laugh too, nodding and laughing
Slack-jawed
This wasn't how things were supposed to be
Why can't I laugh about the thing with the fish?
Why can't I act casual and stand in a corner with a beer
and just be cool like I imagined things?
I cry in the loo
Catch sight of myself in the mirror
Feel like I'm looking at someone else
I quit

I do nothing
Watch Oprah and Dr. Phil every day
Live off government benefits
I've been to the doctor, he prescribed me some pills
I feel hollow
The pills do no good
I go back to the doctor
He refers me to a psychiatric outpatient clinic
My therapist is a social worker who's done a course in cognitive behavioural therapy
She's very unsure of herself
Can't look me in the eye
She asks me what's wrong, why I need to speak to someone
I tell her I spend every waking hour thinking about death, that I dream about it at night
That I hate myself and most other people
That sounds difficult, she says
I tell her it is, but that no one can help me, including her
We'll have to see about that, she says
She draws a bunch of circles and lines on an overhead projector sheet
Explains that our thought patterns can be changed
I psyche her out
Stare at her
Pose critical questions to catch her out
I catch her out

I tell her I have another appointment and walk out
before the end of the session
I don't want to die
I dream of being immersed in my own blood, hacking
at myself with a blunt knife
If only I could just see something through, but I'm
weak and I'm scared
Maybe if I got cancer, I think to myself, but that's easier
said than done
I step out in front of cars without warning and smoke
as many cigarettes as I can get through
I down a triple dose of my psycho pills after dinner
They leave me paralysed
I call the out-of-hours clinic
The woman on the phone tells me I'll be paralysed for
a few hours at worst, but that I'm not going to die
I start to cry
Now I can't even watch TV
Next time I'll jump, I think to myself
I fantasise about the people who'll find me
About broken arms and legs
About the trauma I'll inflict upon them for the rest of
their lives
I fall asleep
When I wake up, it's Christmas Eve
Grandad asks me if I haven't had enough pork ribs
already
I ask him what he means

He tells me I've filled out
I tell him I'm not the only one then run to the
bathroom in tears
The others have a hard time coaxing me out for dessert
and presents
I don't want their stupid fucking presents, I cry
Give them to a Romanian orphanage, I tell them
But I don't mean it
Obviously I want them
I come downstairs
Grandad apologises
I tell them I don't want any dessert, that I'm fat enough
already
We all laugh and I eat two bowls of rice pudding

3

People on the street stare at me
Everywhere I go they stare
I scream at one woman on the tram
Tell her she's a bad person, that it's people like her who are destroying the planet
She looks away
I tell her she can look the other way for what it's worth
She can turn away, but that only makes things worse
I ask if there's something odd about me
She shakes her head
I tell her that she's the one who's odd, with her ugly clothes and her wrinkles
Money can't save her, I tell her
She can't take her fur coat to hell
She ought to take a pickaxe to her own face and bleed it of every last ounce of filler
I tell her that she and everyone she knows and loves is going to die one day and there's nothing she can do about it

She's clutching a bag from a designer shop
I grab it from her and empty the contents onto the floor
A silk dress, a scarf and a blazer
I step all over them
Trample them into the dirty tram floor
I jump off the tram and run
I go into a café
Everyone stares
I go home
Lock the door behind me
Turn off my phone
I'm shaking
Cover up all of the mirrors in the flat
Turn on the TV
Light a cigarette
Turn off the TV
Pull the duvet up around me
Close my eyes
Open them
Close them
Turn the TV back on
There's a documentary on about the Mayan Indians
Their calendar ends in the year 2012, it says
I turn the volume all the way up
They're talking about the number 23
I start putting two and two together
23 is following me
23 is everywhere

I'm piecing things together
Everything is 23 and 23 is everything
I understand more and more just how things fit
together
Never leave the house on the 23rd
I'm scared, but I'm glad I've wrapped my head around
something this important
I talk to Mum
I have to tell her a secret, I say
She needs to watch out for the number 23
That's nonsense, she tells me
I'm furious
Tell her she has to watch her back, that nothing is what
she might think
She asks me what I mean
I can't explain over the phone, I tell her
I have to hang up now, I say
I lie awake at night reading all about the number 23
online
Lots of people have got it all sussed out
Mum wonders if I'm getting any sleep
I lie and tell her I'm sleeping fine
She tells me I don't look well
I tell her it's all relative, that this might be the first time
in my life that I actually am well
I tell her she doesn't look too well herself
I don't leave the flat unless I'm going to McDonalds or
buying cigarettes from the shop

My girlfriend tells me she's worried about me, that she can't handle this
If that's the case then she'll have to find herself a new girlfriend, I tell her
I don't cry anymore
Nothing feels sad
Just strange
Like déjà vu

There's a knock at my door
I don't open it
They knock again, harder this time
They're from the police and I need to open up, they say
I don't need to be scared, they tell me, they're only here to help me
I climb out through the bathroom window
Jump down onto a ledge and scramble down some guttering
I run
It's cold
Minus 20, probably
My feet are bleeding
I run past the Prime Minister's residence
Hop over the railings
There are no guards

I laugh
Ring the doorbell
The Prime Minster opens the door
I introduce myself
Tell him I know that he knows
He looks confused, glances all around
'23,' I say
He looks scared
I slap him
'Wake up, man! It's only a question of time, you need to work with me on this.'
He tries closing the door
I hold it open
He can't close the door on this, I shout
It's no good shutting it out now, it'll soon be too late
He slams the door and locks it
The police have caught up with me
I have to go with them, they tell me, they're not taking me to prison
I cry for the first time in a long, long time

I wake up in a white room
Someone is sitting in a chair
I ask them who they are
It's a woman or a man, I can't tell
They tell me I need to sleep
More people come in
They're talking
I ask for a pen and paper
They flip me over and jab me in the bum with a needle
I tell them I want to speak to a lawyer
They leave
I'm not going to come to any harm here, the person in
the chair tells me
I tell them that it all feels fucking harmful enough so far
Everything is harmful
I ask them if they've seen 23
They tell me I need to get some sleep
I ask them who they are
They leaf through a magazine and tell me that we can
talk again when I wake up

4

Summer on the psych ward
I get through 40 cigarettes a day and a pot of coffee
  every hour
The patients sit out in the garden clutching their cups
  and cigarette packets
I'm sweating and shaking
We talk about electroshock and solitary confinement
Gunnar can't remember his wife's name, he tells us
I start to cry
He pats me on the shoulder and tells me I have bags
  under my eyes
Big dark blue circles
That I need to drink more water
He doesn't have a clue, I scream
He doesn't know me
I drink 2 litres of water a day
But that's a lie
I can't remember the last time I drank any water
I sunbathe topless later that day, trying to turn him on

Gunnar is a Christian
A nurse tells me to put a top on
'It's 40 fucking degrees out here!' I tell her, pointing to the thermometer
'But maybe you like your tits to be white and pasty?'
Her face pales
She looks annoyed
She comes back out with the ward manager
Her name is Reidun
Reidun is a twat
She looks like she hasn't had a decent fuck in decades
They follow me to my room
I write messages to the people outside in lipstick on my window
Draw a picture of Reidun's face with a penis pointing at her mouth
Everyone laughs, everyone except Gunnar
Reidun comes to my room
She's furious, I feel like I'm back at primary school
'What are you going to do, give me detention?' I ask
I realise how childish I'm being, but it feels so right
She tells me I've got no respect, that my behaviour is having a negative effect on the atmosphere on the ward
I tell her she can take her saggy white tits and fuck right off
That her behaviour is having a negative effect on the atmosphere in my room

The old bag squints at me and tells me there'll be consequences for my actions
She slams the door on her way out
There's a Monet print on the bedroom wall
It's ugly
Framed
I try smashing the glass
Jump up and down on it
It's made of plastic, it won't break
Nothing breaks here
I consider the window
Don't have the guts for that
Think to myself that if I were really, properly crazy then I'd have broken the window
I feel angry when I realise I'm not crazy enough for that
I get inside the cupboard
The door won't open again
I hammer on the door
Nobody can hear me
Fucking hell
I sit in the cupboard for an hour before a nurse comes to my room and lets me out
She laughs
It's not funny, I tell her
She tells me that it is quite funny, actually
We both laugh
We sit on the edge of the bed laughing

The nurse laughs until she cries
I have to ask her to stop
She's nice, she has grey hair
We go outside for a smoke
I've had an angry outburst
The senior consultant has come down to see me
I tell him I need to run three laps around the building
If they don't let me, I don't know what I'll do with myself
I tell him I'm feeling oppressed, that it feels like nobody is listening to me
He tells me that's typical for my type of psychosis
The nurse nods
I ask them to shut up about my psychosis and explain to them that this is just an angry outburst, that the odd angry outburst is completely fucking normal, thank you very much
The senior consultant and the nurse are speaking Latin
I ask them to speak Norwegian
The consultant looks at me
A meaningful gaze
Your request to run three laps around the building has been granted, he says, looking cheerful
His sense of humour makes me feel physically sick
On my way out of the room I tell him he's a bastard
I can hear them taking notes
They're scribbling so hard and fast you'd think they were masturbating

I run around the house
A quick first lap
I decide to scream at the top of my lungs for the next two
The other patients stand in the garden cheering me on
My Swedish friend Lisa roars that she's angry too
'FUCK THE OFFICE OF THE PUBLIC GUARDIAN!' she screams
'DEATH TO THE OFFICE OF THE PUBLIC GUARDIAN!'
I scream her words back at her as I dash by
A nurse stands waving her arms, she wants me to quieten down
I run and scream and scream and scream until I collapse in a coughing fit
I go back inside and eat two cheese sandwiches and watch 'Who Wants to be a Millionaire?'
Hassan says that it was cool to see me running around the building like that
'I know,' I tell him
'I don't give a shit.'

Two friends I hardly ever talk to have called me on the ward

They tell me they want to come and see me sometime after four the next day and that they hope I'm doing alright
I'm surprised and pleased
I brag to the nurses and the others who never get any visitors
They give me Oxazepam and I go to bed at eight o'clock to make the time pass more quickly
I wake up at six
The night nurse tells me I have to go back to bed
I tell him he can go fuck himself
I sit in the lounge reading magazines
Counting the minutes
Smoking a cigarette every quarter of an hour
Coffee
Magazines
Clock
Cigarette
Magazines
Clock
Coffee
Cigarette
Morning meeting with Lars the nurse
We're going to take a morning walk, he announces
It's the stupidest idea I've ever heard, but I decide I'll make the effort, just for today
I tell everyone that I have a few hours to kill before my friends are stopping by to visit me

Lisa says she's jealous and lonely
She starts going on about the husband who raped her and held her captive for three months
That's awful, Lars tells her, but that's something for the two of them to talk about later
Lisa shouts about how she's being censored, that this affects everyone
The room goes quiet
Lisa starts to cry
Not normal cries, but high-pitched shrieks that come from somewhere deep inside her
I've never heard anything like it
I start hyperventilating
I have to breathe in and out of a paper bag
They take Lisa away
She mustn't let them inject her with anything, I call out to her as they take her away

It's just me and Lars and Johan who go out for a walk
Johan is a real-life schizophrenic
He touches my bum and tells me he knows it turns me on
It does, but I tell him that's not true and that he has to stop
Lars walks between us to keep Johan at a distance
Johan talks about 9/11 and the fact he has contacts in the States who can prove it was an inside job

Lars tells Johan that he knows the rules, we're not supposed to talk about things like that when we're on our morning walk or out in company
I ask him what we are allowed to talk about when we're out in company
Lars suggests that we talk about where in Norway it's nice to go on holiday
He asks if we've ever been up north and tells us he and his girlfriend are planning a road trip to Lofoten in August
Johan and I start laughing
We're both in hysterics
I've made up my mind that we should fuck
I take his hand
We run away
Lars calls after us, shouts that we have to come back
We can't hear him
We run like the fucking wind
Johan looks as if he's in a world of his own
I tell him it's OK
We're going to fuck, I tell him
I pull him into some undergrowth
Kiss him
He touches my boobs
Paws at them over and over like he's never touched a pair of tits before
I grab his cock
It's huge

I laugh
He asks what I'm laughing at
I tell him I'm happy because he's got a big cock
He laughs too, then hitches up my skirt and pulls down my pants
He shoves two fingers inside me
I unzip his fly
His trousers are filthy, covered in coffee stains
He smells of smoke and like it's been a long time since he last had a wash
It's all the fucking same to me
His mouth is open, it's like he can't believe what's happening
I can't believe it either
I lean over and he pushes his way inside me
I'm so wet
This is fun, I think to myself
This is the fucking life
I push back onto his cock
He makes a weird moaning sound then starts to fuck me
I forget that I exist
He lays me down on my back
Pins me down and bites my tits and my neck
Bites me hard
I tell him to stop
He pins me down and fucks me and bites and bites until I start to scream

I feel the blood dripping from my neck
See blood all around Johan's mouth
He howls like a wolf
I just lie there
Look him in the eye
There's no one home
His eyes are black
He babbles away in what sounds like German
Prattles on and on
He comes inside me then pulls out and runs away
I just lie there
Can't move
Can't feel myself breathing
Just feel hot blood trickling around my throat and pooling at the nape of my neck like sweat
Lars shouts
Hurries through the undergrowth and finds me there
He carries me back to the ward
They give me a tetanus shot and bandage me up
They tell me Johan has been moved to Dikemark high-security hospital and that I need to be kept under observation for the week
I call my friends and tell them I've taken a turn for the worse, that they'll need to stop by some other time

My girlfriend comes to see me
She tells me she's confused, that it seems like I don't love her anymore
I don't love anyone
I tell her it's over
She cries
Her bottom lip quivers
She tells me she doesn't know me anymore and wonders if I even know myself
I tell her I've fucked three of the other patients on the ward, and that I don't believe anyone knows themselves, not really
She tells me I'm the worst person she's ever met
I tell her I agree, but that it's her responsibility to watch who she falls in love with and that it was hardly a smart move falling in love with someone as sick and hollow as I am
I feel the urge to throw my arms around her and tell her nothing I'm saying is true
That I'm stupid and mean and she's good and kind
There's a lump in my throat
I force it down
There's no going back
She holds me close and tells me that she won't give up on us, that we can make it work if I promise to sort myself out
I tell her I'm in love with someone else
That he's just as sick and hollow as I am

I tell her she should go
Tell her not to call me
I wish her luck with everything
Her bottom lip quivers
Her entire lower jaw quivers
Her eyes are puffy and tears run down her cheeks
She sounds short of breath and covers her face with her hands
There's a stabbing in my chest and my skin crawls
I have to squint to see her clearly
'You can't really think that,' she says
'I do. I can think what I want and I think that you should go now.'
She slaps me
I slap my other cheek
She hiccups and tells me she never thought she'd experience anything this fucked up
That she didn't believe people like me actually existed
That I've ruined her life
It feels as if I ought to cry
I force out some high-pitched whimpers and pretend
But I don't shed any tears
She looks at me in disbelief
Turns around and crosses the car park
My head is spinning
I light up and take a walk around the building
Mathias is sitting in the middle of the garden between the pillars that divide the wards

I'm in love with Mathias
He speaks French and has sparkling blue eyes and black hair
I've got butterflies in my stomach
As if she'd never been here
As if I'd never even known her
Nothing means a thing outside of this exact moment
Colours are deeper than they've ever been before
I feel completely and utterly free
I'm wearing a summer dress
Dancing in front of Mathias
He tells me I'm beautiful and asks me if I want to marry him
'I do,' I say, 'of course I do.'
He laughs and sings me an Edith Piaf song
He tells me she was singing about having no regrets
I ask if he has any regrets and he replies that he doesn't have time for that kind of thing
That nobody should have any regrets, that people do the things they do for a reason
We smoke and drink our coffee, leaning against the pillars and looking out onto the garden
He asks if that was my girlfriend who came to visit me
I tell him she was here and she cried and I broke up with her
He asks if I'm OK
Never better, I tell him
'No regrets,' I say

He tells me my hand is shaking
I tell him it's because I'm so in love, because I'm living so intensely in the moment
All of a sudden he gets up to leave
I ask him where he's going
He tells me he needs to go to bed then kisses me on the cheek
I hold him tight
Latch onto him
Cling to him
He laughs, tells me I need to let go, tells me we'll see each other again in the morning
Then he makes his way back to his ward
I feel as if I'm falling
I black out
My skin crawls
I feel sick
A nurse calls out that it's ten o'clock and I need to come back inside
The light on the ward blinds me
I go to my room and curl up under the duvet
Get up again
Curl up under the duvet
Get up again
Lie on the floor
Get up
Lie down
Fall asleep

They've put me on new meds
7 pills in the morning
4 in the middle of the day
9 in the evening
I sound permanently drunk
I can sometimes feel myself dribbling beyond my control
I forget more and more about myself
They inject me with something whenever I'm scared and hear voices
It leaves me with a bruised, sore bum for days
Hard like iron
Nobody ever calls me except for Mum
She looks sad and brings me coca-cola and magazines
She tells me that I'm going to get through this, that I'm the strongest person she knows
She couldn't be more wrong, I think to myself
Mum is wonderful
She's proud of me
She understands that I can't cope with life
She's proud of me anyway
I feel guilty
She has no idea the things that I get up to
She tells me that I'm kind, that I've always been a good girl
I feel sorry for her
She has no idea what she's created
She must be blind

She has no choice
She comes running whenever I call her
Strokes my hair
Chats with me
She's warm and kind and good
She laughs at my psycho jokes
Listens to what the voices are telling me
Takes me seriously
She tells the doctors that they're wrong about my illness, that this is a crisis, not a medical condition
That they need to reduce my medication
The doctors tell me not to listen to Mum
That it's unfortunate but she's too swayed by her own fears to be the kind of person I can really rely on
They ask her not to get involved with my treatment plan

When I sleep, I'm dead
I have no memories
No dreams
Everything is black and heavy like slabs of concrete
Pills
Green and white
Great big things
I take them four at a time
Heave
More at breakfast
More at lunch
More at dinner
I can stare at the wall for five hours at a time without getting bored
Can't be bothered knitting anymore
Can't be bothered talking, just watch as new patients come and go
Can't be bothered brushing my teeth
I wet the bed at night
Overhear a nurse complaining about the smell of my feet
I ask how long I'll be slurring my words
It varies from person to person, they say

5

It's six months since I was placed in compulsory
psychiatric care
I ask if it isn't about time they let me stay on a
voluntary basis
They tell me it's regrettable but it'll be a long time
before I reach that milestone
They tell me I'm going to be moved
I'm being moved to an institution for patients with
chronic mental illness
I ask them if I've got a chronic illness
They tell me that I do, that I'll be on medication for the
rest of my life
That's out of the question, I tell them
Then I'll be on and off psych wards all my life, they say
They also tell me that there's a strong chance that I'd
take my own life
They suggest electroshock therapy
I ask if they've lost their minds
I'm only 20, I insist, but they tell me age is no barrier

They've seen positive outcomes in patients as young as 18
I realise these people are sicker than I ever expected
That I'm going to have to inwardly oppose them
I nod politely and tell them that I'll consider it
I'm being moved in two days' time
I run out and knock on Mathias' window
He comes out
I tell him I'm being moved and that he needs to ask to be moved too
He tells me he'll do it
I pack up my things
Mathias meets me in the garden
He tells me that he can't be moved, but that he'll come and visit me
I cry
He hugs me and thanks me for everything
I know he'll never visit
A taxi arrives to pick me up, a nurse is coming with me
I'm scared, but I feel excited too
We roll up the driveway to the institution
The building is creepy and dark and very old
There's a large Virgin Mary monument on the roof
I ask the nurse if I can't just go back with her
She smiles and takes my bag out of the car
We're met by a fat Finnish woman, the senior consultant
I have to pinch myself

During admission she tells me I'm going to be staying
in section 2
The first week will be in seclusion
I ask her why
They tell me it's so they can observe my condition
I feel a tingling in my stomach
I open my mouth to say something but I realise that it's
better to keep my thoughts to myself here
They follow me
There are no pictures on the walls of my room
It's cold
There's a shared bathroom
It stinks of piss and there's shit all over the floor
There's a smoking room
Yippee
A guy is sitting inside
His name is Lasse
He's talking to the radiator
I ask what he's up to
He tells me there's someone living in the radiator and
the air conditioner
That they're talking shit about him
I ask what they're saying
He says they're telling him to shut up
I tell him he ought to tell them to shut up right back
Lasse laughs
He tells me that would lead to some serious
consequences

He explains that they once started eating away at his brain
It's dinner time
The food here is disgusting
Everything reeks of piss
A girl called Trude sits watching me and growling
I meow back at her
She throws a cup of water in my face then gets up and takes off her trousers
She's not wearing any underwear
She plants her bum on the table and rubs it against the table top
'Like daaaaaaaaaat,' she snarls
I start to laugh
She tells me she's going to kill me
I tell her to go for it, that it's all the fucking same to me
Onc of the patients tells me Trude did too much ecstasy and acid back in the 90s, that she's been here for 6 years now
Trude's hair stands up on end and she's got piercings all over
I want to die
I'm followed out into a garden
All the staff here are called support workers
My support worker is 23 years old
She's got blonde hair and fake boobs
She hasn't got a clue how to do her job
I ask her about all sorts of things

I ask her if her tits are real
She tells me it's better if we don't discuss her
But we can talk about me, of course
She asks what I want to do with my life, what I want to be
I need to think about it
I tell her I want to be an actor
It's the only thing that pops into my head
'Oh, that's cool,' she says
I walk to the opposite end of the garden and sit down on a bench
Chain-smoke four cigarettes
I'm going to be an actor, of course I am, I think to myself
It sounds like a plan
I think about Leonardo
I feel the same tingling I felt back when there was nothing but fields as far as the eye could see
I throw up
Feel restless
I want to start acting today
Now
This very minute
I feel as if things might just work out
The same things probably happened to Leonardo DiCaprio once upon a time, I think to myself

I don't dare use the toilet
There's a 60-year-old man in the next room
He walks around with his trousers slung so low that his crack's always on show and he's constantly carrying a bowl of water
He babbles away to himself
I don't understand a word of whatever language he's speaking
I sit in the smoking room with Lasse, Trude and a boy my age
His name is Kjell and he's not even a little bit crazy
He's just a junkie
I'm glad Kjell is here
Lasse and Trude like each other
They laugh and yelp and Lasse sits with his hands over his ears

We have a meeting to discuss my treatment plan
I tell them how much I hate my pills
That I can't face popping 19 of the things every day
They tell me there's an injection I can have instead
I'd only need it twice a month
I tell them I want it
Can't wait to ditch the pills
My time in seclusion is over

I'm allowed four hours' unescorted leave each day
In the evening I go to a pub down the road with Kjell
and a few of the others
We all drink
We get hammered
When someone asks who we are and what we're up to,
we tell them we've come from the mental hospital
just up the road
That we're out on unescorted leave
People get scared, it's hilarious
We drink and drink and drink
Our drugs mix with the alcohol and we experience all
kinds of new highs
Kjell and I fuck in the toilet
We get thrown out
We roam the streets
Kjell buys speed
We both take some
We march along, nothing can tire us out
We march all the way to the palace
We throw gravel at the guards
Run away
Buy eggs from a newsagent
Walk to the city hall and smash them against the walls
Walk to Aker Brygge and topple all of the chairs
outside the cafes
Buy more eggs and pelt the windows
Sit in front of the National Theatre

I lay out my acting plans for Kjell
He tells me he thinks it's a good idea
That he thinks I'd make a good actor
I put on a little performance just for him
Sing and dance and make up a monologue on the spot
Kjell claps
We take more speed
Fuck in the palace gardens
Buy hash and lie on our backs looking upwards
We gaze up at the stars
Fall asleep

I'm put in seclusion for another week
Silje the silicon support worker tells me it wasn't exactly
clever running off like that
I tell her I've never been one for doing the clever thing
That I just do what I do
She tells me I have to accept the consequences if that's
the case
Whenever we're out in the garden, I smoke my way
through an entire 10-pack
It's cold outside
Silje doesn't smoke
It annoys her that I do

This is my freedom, I tell her, she can keep her opinions
to herself
She tells me I can smoke in the smoking room
I tell her that I need a change of scenery
She lets me know that tomorrow is the day I'll be
starting my new meds
Two weeks pass
I've stopped taking the pills
Everything's good
I'm good
I can't hear any voices in my head
I'm not sad
I'm not happy
I don't feel as if anyone's out to get me
There are no thoughts in my head at all
Zero
Not one
There's just me and the hollowness inside
Leonardo feels so far away, so stupid
I play cards with Trude
She wins every time
We don't talk
I don't talk to anyone
Kjell is transferred to another ward
I sleep and eat normally
Silje asks me how I am
I tell her I feel fine
The doctors tell me I can be discharged before too long

I've been here for 3 months now
I can tell that they're pleased with themselves
I ask them when my thoughts will return
I tell them I'll be needing them if I'm going to get anywhere with my acting plans
That you can't make it as an actor without any thoughts or feelings
They tell me that a reduced emotional spectrum is one of the side effects of my new medication
I ask if it's normal for someone's thoughts to disappear
They've nothing to say to that
They should come back in due course, they tell me
They ask me if I feel better now than I did before
I tell them that depends on how they'd define 'better'
They tell me that I ought to reconsider my career plans
I'm going to get angry now, I think to myself
But I don't get angry, not even a bit, just tell them that they're entitled to their opinion
They tell me they'd advise against it in the strongest possible terms
I can't be bothered arguing with them
I've barely got the energy to stand up
I make for the door
Feel a sense of dread smouldering inside me
I do my best to slam the door behind me on my way out

I leave the ward
I've been discharged
I'm going home to start my life
I feel as if my life is over

6

I live in a little flat by Majorstua
I've decided that I definitely won't be continuing with my course of medication
It's not a good idea, not now that I've made a plan
I'm going to make it, I just know it
I'm going to make it by myself
I tell Mum that this is worse than any depression or psychosis
I tell her that I'd rather hear voices for the rest of my life than feel nothing at all
She tells me that she understands, but that I need to think things through very carefully
I tell her it's hard to think things through when I have no thoughts
I tell her that I've decided to become an actor
She sounds pleased but she looks worried
I tell her about Leonardo
Mum laughs and says it's a good idea
That she's always thought I was creative and outgoing

That it might just suit me nicely
She takes me to meet a woman who talks about loving yourself
About being codependent
I don't get it
I wonder if she's found religion
She tells me it's important to remain open to alternative therapies, especially now that I want to become an actor
I have to remain open, Mum says
I have to listen to those who want the best for me
I tell her it's a load of rubbish
I can take care of myself, I tell her
I don't need her or her weird cult
Mum says I don't want to get better
I stop taking her calls
The doctor from the outpatient clinic calls to remind me about my next injection
The feeling has started to return to my body
I've started thinking again
Constantly thinking
Thoughts sweep through me
It's as if I'm getting high
Getting high off the sun, off the night, off people on the street
I've never appreciated being alive the way I do now
I fall in love with someone different every day
I follow them around

I think about Mathias
I decide that he's my soulmate
Don't sleep, just scribble in my notebook instead
Write terrible, sentimental poetry
The feelings inside me are so intense and unruly that it feels like they might wipe me out at any second
That my heart might just stop right out of the blue
There's a fire inside me
This is nuclear warfare
I look Mathias up online
Find out where he lives
It's just down the street from here
I go to his building
Sit outside for two hours
He doesn't come out
I delay going home with every half hour that passes
It feels pointless giving up after staying for so long
I sit there all night long
Run out of cigarettes
Go to the corner shop whilst keeping an eye on the door of his building
Buy a packet of crisps and a can of coke and two packs of 20 cigarettes
I can't face the prospect of going home
If he gets back and realises I've been sitting here for 48 hours, he'll know how much I love him, I think to myself
I walk up to the doorbell

Don't dare ring it
Press it anyway
Silence
No answer
He must still be on the psych ward, I think to myself

I buy a six-pack of beer at the supermarket
Go home and listen to music
Have a party for one
Dance around
Jump up and down on the sofa
Buy another six beers
Night falls
I take a walk
Look for anyone else out there who can't sit still
I go down to Blitz
There might be others down there who are awake, I think to myself
And there are
I go inside
I'm wearing a nightie with an ugly hoodie over the top
It looks as if everyone here has forgotten to get dressed before coming out
I spot a boy in the crowd
One of Mum's friend's sons
We used to play together when we were five years old
He has red hair and he's much taller than when I saw him last

He looks at me, recognises me
Comes over and hugs me
I like him
Ask him if I can call him Red
He'd like that, he tells me
We go outside and smoke a joint
We both have the same fire inside
We babble away, louder and louder
Talk over one another in our excitement
We laugh at what an amazing coincidence it is to meet like this, agree that there's something significant about it all
He tells me his birthday is the 23rd June
I laugh out loud, hysterical, tell him it's incredible
That it's all the fucking proof we could ever need
He couldn't agree more
He tells me that he has nowhere to go, that he's run away from home
I tell him he's welcome to stay with me

We watch films and smoke weed in bed together
We have sex
He reminds me of Jorg
I tell him that he reminds me of someone
He holds me close and tells me that I don't remind him of anyone at all, tells me that's what he likes so much about me
He marches down the street carrying a big red flag
I admire him
I cut my hair short in the bathroom
I feel as if I'm chopping down a tree
I start to cry
He tells me that I'm pretty
He takes me to a rally
We shout out loud
I don't know what we're demonstrating for or against
I just shout at the top of my lungs
Everyone is angry
It's amazing
I feel as if I'm at the forefront of something important
At the forefront of my own existence
At the forefront of a general sense of anger
I'm at the forefront of the idea that life can be amazing and awful all at once
One day he tells me that he's off to a confidential meeting with his political organisation
He never comes back
I call his mother and ask if she knows where he is

She tells me she doesn't but it's very important that I call her when I do hear from him
That he's not well
I feel all alone
I can't feel the fire I felt before
I try taking a walk at night, but every move I make feels so heavy
I go home
Fall asleep
Wake up two days later
Mum calls
She's worried about me
Tells me she has to see me
She tells me she's coming over
I shower, tidy the flat
Put on some make up
I make coffee and buy biscuits
Mum smells nice
She feels like a Saturday morning, like a warm breeze
I start crying as soon as I set eyes on her
She ruffles my hair and tells me I look great
'You're so cool,' she says, 'everything suits you.'
She tells me that I'm looking well
Her poor judgement surprises me
I tell her things are fine, that life is quiet, stable
The lie makes my stomach ache
She looks pleased, proud
Tells me she's always known that I'm strong and unique

I tell her that I have a group therapy session, that I have to go now
She hugs me
I leave her coffee cup sitting where she put it down for the rest of the week
Find Jorg's phone number online
Tap it into my phone but don't call him
I dream about the future
About how I've imagined things, about everything that's going to happen
Think to myself that maybe I ought to make a start on things
It seems so distant and unfamiliar, but not as distant as it always has
I submit an application to drama school
Fill in the paperwork at the library
They ask about previous experience
About why I want to be an actor
The lies spill forth
I write that I've had a lot of experience over the years, that I can't live my life without art
I don't write that I want to be in the spotlight
I don't write that I just want to be seen and heard
I don't send them my educational qualifications
I'm terrified
The drama school gets back to me
They invite me to audition
I feel unsure

It dawns on me that I'm planning on doing something I
know nothing about
I haven't got a clue
I don't know how somebody is supposed to act
I don't know what makes anyone somebody at all
I don't know how somebody is supposed to live, to be,
to think, to feel
I decide to go to the audition even though I have no
idea who I am

7

The audition is in two weeks
I practise the piece I'm going to perform every day
It's Jorg's birthday
I write him a letter
I burn a CD and slip it inside the envelope before posting it to him
I sit on some steps on Bogstadveien drinking coffee
I can see Mathias over the road, he's walking down the street
I run down the steps and across the road to chase him down
I catch hold of his coat flap just as he's about to step into a shop
He turns around, looks at me
I hide my face in my hands
I can't bear for him to look me in the eye
He says hello
'Hi,' I say
'How's it going?' he asks

I can tell from the way he says it that he wishes the ground would swallow him up
I ask him where he's been
At his parents' house, he says
I tell him I live just over the road
'I see,' he replies
I ask him if he wants to meet up sometime
Take a walk together, maybe
He doesn't think that would be a good idea, he says
I'm breathing quickly, too quickly, hide my face in my hands again
I ask why not
Tell him I think it's a very good idea
That I miss him
He looks away
He tells me I have to stay away from him
I ask him why he's saying that, remind him that he asked me to marry him once
He tells me that was just something he said, that he wasn't well at the time
He tells me he's got a girlfriend, that he's not in love with me
I push him into a clothing rail
He shouts at me, calls me a stupid little arsehole
I run all the way home
Sprain my ankle on my way up the stairs
A neighbour comes out, wonders what's happened
I tell him to go back inside and fuck off while he's at it

He tells me I need to calm down
I crawl up the rest of the stairs and let myself in
Trash my flat
Smash all of my CDs
Watch the cases shatter as they hit the wall
Smash everything apart from the windows, the TV, a lamp and a cup
Throw myself onto the bed
Bury my face in my pillow
Punch and punch and punch
Punch myself
Tear up my audition letter
Scratch at my arms
I lie there for two days straight
The doorbell rings
It's Red
He steps inside
His face is swollen
He's limping
I ask him where his flag is
I can't tell anyone that he's here, he says
That's fine, I tell him
He asks if he can stay
I tell him he can, but that my life is at least as fucked up as his
He tells me he doubts that
He climbs into the bed beside me
We lie side-by-side, gazing at one another

I ask what happened to his face
He tells me he was beaten up
He asks what happened to my arms
I tell him I was beaten up too
He kisses me and undresses me
Fills me up with red
We make love
It's therapy
We buy beer at the shop, search among the CDs on the floor for any that haven't been smashed to pieces
We find a few to listen to
Hop into bed
It feels like being home alone
We jump and fuck and laugh and play
I tell him about Mathias
He says that Mathias is stupid not to want to marry me
He asks if we shouldn't just get married instead
Of course we should, I tell him, let's get married and make tiny little redheads together
He laughs
We wake to the sound of knocking at the front door
Our mothers
We need to let them in, they shout
I open the door
They rush inside
Mum looks around the room
She starts crying

She pulls me close and says she never should have left me
I ask what she means by that
She strokes my head and holds me close without saying a word
I feel angry
Tell them they've no right to barge in on us like this
That this is my home
I ask them to leave
Red is staring at the wall
His mother is just standing there like an idiot
Mum tells me she's going to need to call the ward
I tell her she can call them if she likes, but I'm no danger to myself or anyone else
That I'm an adult now
That I've got an audition for a place at drama school two weeks from now
Mum looks at me sympathetically
I ask her what's wrong
That's good to hear, she tells me, but I can't go to my audition looking the way I do now
I tell her that I can, just watch me, I say
They ask us if we want to go back home with them
Absolutely not, we tell them, we're fine as we are
We politely ask them to leave, then we tell them that if they won't go of their own accord we'll have to call the police
They leave

Red asks if we shouldn't just go down to city hall together right now and get married
Fuck yes, let's do it, I tell him
We hop on the tram
The woman at the reception desk tells us we have to make an appointment
This isn't Las Vegas, she says
We're disappointed
We make an appointment
I call Mum and tell her I'm getting married
That she's welcome to come along to the city hall on Saturday
She starts crying
Tells me I'm not well
I shriek at her, tell her to show me some support or go to hell
I hang up
We go to a bar to celebrate
Red suggests that we go to the theatre
I throw my arms around him
They're showing Romeo and Juliet on the main stage at the National Theatre
I start crying the moment I step into the foyer and don't stop until I'm back outside again afterwards
Red tells me that I need to go to my audition
I sob and tell him that I haven't got the guts
He tells me he'll come with me, but that I have to do it
I promise him I will

Dad calls
He tells me that he's spoken to Mum and heard that
I'm getting married
I tell him that's right, that he can come if he really
wants to
He asks what I'm playing at
I'm not playing at anything, I tell him, but I'll hang up
now if he has any more objections
His tone changes
He speaks more softly
It's not his intention to judge, he says, but might I be
rushing into things, even just a little?
I don't want to talk about it, I tell him, but he's
welcome to come on Saturday
He sighs into the receiver and tells me he'll think about
it

I call an old school friend to tell her I'm getting married
She seems far away, she's playing along, but I can tell
that she's desperate to get off the phone
She tells me she'd love to come, but she's been invited
to a birthday party on Saturday
She wishes me luck
I lie and tell her I've been offered a place at drama
school
I ask how things are going at the nursing home,
whether she's found the perfect Volvo to suit her
middle-of-the-road life yet

She falls silent
I tell her I never liked her anyway
That I hope she has a rubbish time at the party
I hang up before she has a chance to reply
I wander around the city looking for a wedding dress
Make my way into a second-hand shop on Storgata
I find a floral silk dress and a tulle skirt and an old crocheted tablecloth to wear as a veil
I feel happy, excited
I'm in love
I'm going to marry Red

We stand outside the city hall at ten o'clock on Saturday morning
We're waiting for our mothers
We give them half an hour
Nobody comes
Red is wearing an old suit that's slightly too big for him
He's carrying a bunch of flowers for me, lily of the valley
He tells me I'm the most beautiful thing he's ever laid eyes on
I hug him so hard that I lose my breath
We need witnesses
We ask a few passers-by if they'll do it
They tell us they'd be happy to

We don't have any rings, but I've bought him a nice pin badge
He's bought me a necklace with a heart pendant
And then we're married, just like that
I faint on the way out
Red lifts me up, tells me it's alright
We sit on a bench together and cry
We hold hands, squeeze each other tight
Afterwards we go to the theatre café and blow almost every last krone of my benefits
We talk about where to go on our honeymoon
I suggest going to India and never coming back
He laughs and reminds me about my audition
If I don't get into drama school then we'll go to India, I tell him
If I do get in then we should spend a weekend in Copenhagen or Amsterdam, he says
A little more within our price range, he reminds me
I agree, but tell him I'd prefer Paris or Barcelona
Paris or Barcelona it is, then, he says
We go to a pub and drink too much before making for home
We lie awake all night long, gazing at one another
We make love over and over
I laugh at the idea of us making love
He laughs too, says it makes us sound like an old married couple

We laugh about the fact that we are a married couple,
old or otherwise
I tell him he'll always be a boy to me
He tells me I'll always be his girl
I tell him about Jorg, and the fact I've had a girlfriend
in the past
I tell him I've been horrible to a lot of people, that I've
probably slept with 20 people without a condom
He likes to hear me talk about my life
It doesn't make him jealous
I tell him about all of the pain inside me, and the fact
that I sometimes hear voices
He tells me that he hates himself
I tell him that I hate myself too
We agree on the fact that we don't hate each other, that
we each think the other is the best person we know,
and that must mean we're not so horrible after all
It feels nice
It's nice to be the best person someone knows

8

It's the day before my audition
My stomach aches
Red brings me cola and makes me soup and tells me everything is going to be fine
I curl up in bed
I feel as if I'm dying
He tells me it's all in my head
I ask him to go away, tell him I want to be alone
He tells me he can't do that because he loves me and we're married now
I tell him he doesn't love me, that it's all just an illusion
He laughs and tells me to stop that before he gets annoyed
I tell him I've realised I don't love him after all, that I want a divorce
He tells me he's going to count to three and that I should take back what I said before he's done
He counts to three
I want to apologise

My stomach aches even more
I don't apologise
I tell him he can pack up all of his crap and get out of my flat, that I never want to see his ugly face again
He makes for the door
Wishes me luck with my audition, tells me he'll forgive me when I come to my senses
I scream at him to get out
That I won't be coming to my senses
That he's a bad person and the fact that he loves me proves just what kind of dysfunctional moron he really is
I tell him I couldn't give a shit about the audition, that I'm getting out of here, that I'm going to leave the country and set up somewhere far away from him
He leaves
I breathe into my pillow
Hold my stomach
Don't know how long I spend lying there
He comes back, lies down beside me
Pulls me close
Tells me I can say whatever I want to him
That he won't leave me, no matter what
I tell him I'm going to kill him
He just holds me
I hit him
He holds my hands until I stop fighting him
He strokes my hair

I must tell him I hate him at least a hundred times
He tells me I can say what I like, but he loves me all the same
He knows who I am, he tells me
He's got no idea, I say
I don't know what else I can say to make him leave
I just lie there, let him hold me
He kisses my stomach
Tells it to buck up its ideas and give me a break
I laugh
Tell him he's an idiot
He agrees with me
He can't wait to see me up on stage, he says
I'm not going to the audition, I tell him
He tells me I need to get some sleep
I apologise
He says that he forgives me, that I'm still the best person he knows
I fall asleep

I wake up at six
Red is lying beside me, fully dressed and fast asleep
I've woken in a cold sweat
I lie there, staring up at the ceiling
Can't face the thought of moving
My thoughts are racing
My stomach aches
I tell my body it has to move
Nothing happens
I lie there until seven
Take a shower
Drink two cups of coffee and have a cigarette
I look over at Red
Feel guilty
Take the tram to Grünerløkka
Buy a cup of coffee and a pastry from 7-Eleven
My hands are clammy
I close my eyes as I walk
March along as fast as I can
A woman walks straight into me
There's coffee all down the front of my dress
I scream at her
Ask if she's a complete moron
Tell her I've got somewhere important to be
I burst into tears
I need to sit down
She tells me I need to watch my heart, the way I'm
going

I'm shaking, prickling all over
Red calls
He asks me where I am
I tell him I'm on my way to my audition but my dress is covered in coffee and I'm sitting on the pavement in tears
He tells me to relax, that he can bring me another dress
'I WANT THIS DRESS, THIS IS THE DRESS I WANTED TO WEAR!' I shout
I hang up
I call him back
Apologise
Tell him he can bring the green dress that's lying on the sofa
He laughs and tells me he'll be there in 20 minutes
I carry on walking and try breathing into my belly
I don't really know what it means to breathe into my belly
I've just heard people say it
TAKE A DEEP BREATH
LET IT FILL YOUR BELLY
The breath just stops at my diaphragm
It always has
I make my way inside the drama school, a large, factory-like building
I brighten up
Meet a few of the others there for the auditions
They ask what I do when I'm not doing this

I tell them I'm on benefits
They giggle nervously, look away
They ask what happened to my dress
I tell them some madwoman barged into me on my way here
I lie and tell them I gave her what for and made her reimburse me for the damage
I tell them this dress once belonged to Brigitte Bardot
They laugh
I ask them why they're laughing and they tell me that I'm funny
I'm not trying to be funny, I tell them
They apologise and leave
I strike up conversation with a girl there on her own, her name is Kari
She seems nervous
I tell her she needn't be
That I've done this lots of times before and it only feels like this to begin with
I tell her she just has to breathe into her belly and look them in the eye
She thanks me for my help
I tell her it was my pleasure
It's reassuring to act like an old pro
She asks how much acting I've done before, tells me that she goes to the same college as all of the big names

I tell her I've spent a year touring with a company in
Eastern Europe
That I attended a strict school in Russia before that
I don't know where it all comes from
She asks if we used Stanislavski's system
I think for a moment before telling her yes
I've no idea who Stanislavski is
She starts speaking to me in Russian
Tells me her mother is from there
I pretend to need the toilet and tell her I have to go
I splash my face with water and focus on my reflection
in the mirror
Tell myself I'm funny and pretty
By the time I step back outside, Red has arrived with
my dress
I leap up onto his back and tell everyone that he's my
husband
They nod politely and say hello
I take him outside for a smoke
He hugs me and tells me to relax
That I'm far prettier and cooler than everyone else here
I tell him that his red hair gives me strength
He pulls out a few strands and hands them to me
I stuff them inside my bra
I ask him if he can wait for me to finish up here
He tells me that's no problem at all
They tell us to gather round so they can give us some
information

My hands are still wet and it takes everything I have to say yes in a normal voice when they get to my name on the register
I can't quite regulate my volume, no matter how hard I try
I'm in trouble now, I think to myself, I'll never make it as an actor if I can't even sound normal saying yes
They tell us they're going to introduce the panel
There's a woman there, staring at me
It's the woman from the coffee incident
I want to disappear, to shrivel up
She gives me a forced smile
I act as if nothing's wrong
Smile back at her, relaxed
I'm shaking
They stick a list of our names up on the wall with times for us to go in and perform our monologues
My slot's not for another hour
I go out to see Red
I tell him that we can go home right now before explaining to him about the woman on the panel of judges
He tells me not to give a shit, just to go for it no matter what
We agree that I'll do just that
Red kisses me, lifts me up, tells me to seize the moment
I take a seat outside the room
Feel as if I'm awaiting my own execution

Kari walks by and says something in Russian
I give her the thumbs up
My breath is still there, just above my diaphragm
There's no trace of oxygen in my belly
They call my name, not the coffee woman luckily, but an older man with a walking stick and a limp
He seems nice
I shake his hand, make sure my grip is firm and precise
He praises my handshake
I tell him his could do with some work
He laughs and tells me he'll give that some thought
We make our way down a strange, narrow hallway and through a heavy door leading out onto the stage
It's like a birth
The stage light is harsh, intense
I shake hands with the coffee woman without hesitating
Look her straight in the eye and tell her it was nice bumping into her this morning, so to speak
She laughs
I feel elated as I greet the final member of the panel, a bald man with a huge beard
A flurry of remarks rush through my mind but I press my lips together and force the words back where they came from
They tell me I can begin whenever I'm ready

Everything turns black

I don't remember a single thing that happens before I leave the stage

I try to read the expressions of those around me
They all look wrapped up in their own thoughts
I see that as a good sign
Kari runs over asking me how it went
I tell her it went well, that I received a standing ovation
Kari looks defeated, I wish her luck and tell her to stand tall
I run out to Red
Collapse into his arms
He asks me what happened
I tell him I can't remember a thing, that everything went black, but that they laughed at the jokes I remember making before blacking out
That's good, he says
I tell him it doesn't sound all that good to me
That I've probably completely embarrassed myself
He tells me I've always had a tendency to amplify a crisis
We have a drink at the pub
I tell Red that I love him, that I didn't mean to be so hard on him
I tell him that I'm only ever horrible to him because I love him
He tells me he's not going to leave me
He tells me that I'm strong, a good person

That he's proud of me
I feel something in my belly, something warm and good
It radiates throughout my arms and legs
My head and my chest
I'm proud of myself, too

9

There's a letter for me in the post
It's from Jorg, the handwriting gives it away
I put it inside my bag
Don't have the nerve to open it
Red asks if I've heard back from drama school
I tell him no, but that I don't want to talk about it
That's fine, he says
He rubs my shoulders
Tells me I'm feeling tense, that I ought to take up meditation
I tell him he never has anything worthwhile to say, that he should stop going to rallies and shouting about God knows what every week
He tells me it wasn't meant as a personal attack
That actually he was just trying to be thoughtful
That he just wants the best for me
I don't know what to say
He's right
Red tells me he's getting tired of me pushing him away

Tired of the way I don't seem to respect him
He gets up and pulls on his coat
Tell me that he needs to take a walk to calm himself
down
That I should spend that time thinking about what he's
just said
I tell him I couldn't care less about any of it
That I won't be thinking about anything he's just said,
that I've never heard such bullshit like it in my life
That it couldn't be any further from the truth, and that
actually I respect him too much
I tell him that if anything, I respect him less now that
he's revealed how stupid he really is
He tells me he'll be back in an hour and slams the door
on his way out
I look at the wall and curse at Red in Latin I remember
reading in a book about magic I once found on
Jorg's bookshelf
He returns after an hour and a half
He's looking down at his feet
I ask him to look at me
He tells me he's not happy
He thinks I treat him like shit
He's tired of feeling as if he's being tossed around
inside an emotional tumble dryer
He's trying to show me as much love as he possibly can
He needs to be shown a little love now and then, too
I don't know what to say or do

I tell him he needs to hold out a little longer for me
He tells me that he doesn't know if he's good enough for me, that it feels like I don't like him, that it's like he's not important to me at all
He starts to cry
He sobs and sinks to the floor
I freeze
I feel an urge to punch him, to shove him against the door head-first
To tell him that I hate him, that he should fuck off before I kill him
But still I want to comfort him, to hold him, to tell him he's kind and good and that I love him more than anything else on this planet
That I want to take care of him
To stroke his hair
To tell him I'll do whatever it takes to keep us together
But I can't do any of those things
I just stand there, staring at Red as he sobs into his leather jacket
Eventually I lay a hand on his head
'Sorry,' I say
He pulls me down beside him and holds me tight, burying his face into my jumper
He asks me if I love him
I open my mouth to answer
My voice stops in my throat, muffled and strange-sounding

I do, I whisper
I've no idea if what I'm saying is true
Red tells me he made a promise to stay by my side for better or worse
I tell him if that's true then he's dug himself one hell of a deep grave
More likely for worse than for better
He laughs, removes his jacket and picks me up, then carries me over to the bed
He tells me that when things are for the better, they're so good that they're worth dying for
I tell him he ought to write a song and enter the Eurovision Song Contest
Or form his own boyband, maybe
We playfight
I hit him too hard, as usual
We have to stop
We watch TV
I think about the letter Jorg sent me, tucked away inside my bag

Red returns from one of his rallies
He's behaving oddly
I feel a stabbing in my chest
I ask if anything much happened at his rally
He says no
I tell him he's acting differently
He tells me he's been smoking weed
I tell him it's something else
He tells me he's tired
I ask him if he wants to have sex
He tells me he can't be bothered
That's not good enough, I tell him
That's just how it is for now, he says, we can have sex tomorrow
Red falls asleep
I pick up his phone and go through his messages
I find lots from a girl called Hedda
She writes that she likes him and wants to meet up with him again
She thanks him for coming to the rally
Hedda writes that she wants to see him on Thursday
That they could grab a coffee or a beer in the city
I'm shaking
I find messages dating back several weeks
I feel sick
I go to the toilet and stick my fingers down my throat
Lie down
Get back up

Throw up again
I gaze at Red until I fall asleep
Red is so hungover the next day that he does nothing but lie in bed
I ask him again if he wants to have sex, tell him I need him inside me now
He tells me he's sorry but he doesn't feel up to it
I start touching myself in front of him
He laughs and kisses me half-heartedly
Tells me he's really not in the mood
I ask what he's doing on Thursday
Tell him I've got something nice planned
That sounds good, he says, but he'll need to check because he's got a meeting that day
I'm shaking hard now
Ask him what kind of meeting
He tells me his political organisation is having a get-together
Shaking shaking shaking
I scream at him to get out
He asks what's up with me
I tell him his lies are making me sick
He asks what I mean and says he doesn't know what I'm talking about
I tell him to shut up, that I know what he's up to
He pulls on his coat and tells me that I'm crazier than he first thought, that he can't take any more of this
I collapse into a heap on the floor

I lie there in the foetal position
Scream
Can't hear myself anymore
Can't feel anything but my powerlessness to stop myself
 screaming
It's someone else who's screaming
I'm underwater
Perfect silence
I'm in my mother's womb
I float around
I'm weightless
I'm weightless
I gurgle
I've got a twin
The twin dies
I'm scared
I don't want to be born
I'm born anyway
Red is waiting for me at the end of the channel
He's smiling from ear to ear
He picks me up and eats my umbilical cord, he's
 gurgling too
He tosses me up into the air
He misses me and I fall to the ground
My forehead is deformed
He doesn't want a deformed child, he says
He sends me to a foster home
I awaken to find myself falling

I'm weightless
Bang
I can't feel my body
I laugh
So many people
Red and blue
White
Red has moved out
I'm eating away at him, he says
Making him ill
I've had a letter from drama school
I've not made it to the next round of auditions
They give no reason why
Just offer their apologies, wish me better luck next time
Of course
What was I thinking
It was a hopeless endeavour
I sit on the lawn outside the psych unit
Grind oxazepam between my teeth
I've broken my arm and my foot
Needed three stitches in my head
I'm lucky to be alive, the doctors say
They're idiots, every last one of them
They don't realise that I'm actually very unlucky to be alive

They don't realise that I'm wasting taxpayer's money, frittering it away on alcohol and bad habits, taking up a bed that could be given to somebody with a real desire to live and get help
I don't want help
I like it at rock bottom
I'm drowning in my own ego
It feels glorious
I love how it feels not to give a shit about anyone, myself included
I make up my mind never to love anyone ever again
I make up my mind to live as a hermit and shack up in a cave in the woods
Either that, or to get lots of cats or birds, to live out my days as a creepy old woman with dirty fingernails who stinks of piss
I laugh
My ribs ache
Lisa is back on the ward too
She writes on my plaster cast with a marker pen
'Lead Consultant Karl Holm is a paedo!' she writes
We laugh ourselves silly
She strokes my hair and tells me I'm the prettiest thing she's ever seen, that I need to get better and go out into the world and act
She can tell I'm going to be just fine, she says
I ask how she knows
She tells me she's psychic

I tell her that I can't trust her psychic powers if that's
what she thinks is going to happen
That it's one of the stupidest things I've heard her
come out with
'Look at me,' I say
Lisa laughs and pokes my cast
She tells me I need to get better anyway, that she wants
me to be well
I look Lisa in the eye
It's the last time I'll do that
I just know I'm not going to see her again
I hug her

I don't know who I am
I've gone too far
I've crossed over to the other side
I see everything all at once
I see everyone all at once
I think every thought all at once
I'm weightless yet heavy
I'm defeated yet determined
I give up
I stand up
I give my all
I cry and I laugh
I eat then throw up, food feels like poison
I spit out my coffee
Spray it all over the walls of the ward
I throw cups at the other patients
I lie on the floor
I crawl and kick
I feel sick
I faint
I come around and lament the fact that I'm alive
I faint again
Throw up all over the ward floor
Clutch at my stomach
I'm inside an empty drum
I'm being tossed around, over and over
I can't I can't
I can't I can't

THIS IS THE DAY I DIE
THIS IS THE DAY I DIE
'You're not going to die.'
YES I AM I'M DYING I'M DYING
SAVE ME SAVE ME SAVE ME
I DON'T KNOW WHERE I AM
'You're in safe hands.'
NO
I'M IN UNSAFE HANDS
I WANT TO GO BACK
I TAKE IT BACK
I TAKE IT BACK HELP ME
I WANT TO GO BACK
HELP ME
HELP ME
WHY ISN'T ANYONE DOING ANYTHING
HELP ME, FOR FUCKS SAKE, HELP ME
'We're helping you. The drugs will kick in soon.
Take nice deep breaths, let the breath fill your belly.'
LET THE BREATH FILL MY BELLY ARE YOU
STUPID I CAN'T
FUCK, CAN'T BREATHE
HELP
WHAT WHAT WHAT AM I SUPPOSED TO DO
I CAN'T FEEL MY BODY
'That's because you're breathing too fast. You need
to slow it down.'
I'M FAINTING

'No, you're fine, just take some deep breaths.'

MUM

WHERE'S MUM

I WANT MY MUM

MUM

HE

L

P

'Someone's calling your mother now. She'll be here soon. We need to give you another injection, do you understand?'

NO DON'T TOUCH ME HELP

DON'T

PLEASE

I DON'T WANT

NO NO NO

I'M NOT HERE

'Do you know what day it is?'

IT'S JUDGEMENT DAY

I'm dying

'That's the medication kicking in. You're not dying. I promise you, you're not dying.'

I'm. Dying.

Red

Red

Red

'Breathe.'

RED

DEAD

NO I CAN'T

'What do you mean?'

IS RED DEAD?

IS HE DEAD NO NO NO

'Red isn't dead, dear. Red's alive.'

DO YOU PROMISE

'I promise. You'll drift off in a minute.'

Do you promise

Do you

Promise

'There, she's asleep now.'

Life is long, I think to myself
This can't possibly be it, I think to myself
I'd always pictured things so differently, I think to myself
I'll soon be 21
I'm dreading turning 30
I regret everything I've ever done
One of my secondary teachers at parents' night once said that I could do anything I set my mind to
I want to confront him, to ask what the hell he was talking about
Do they say that kind of thing about every brat with behavioural difficulties?
I explode
I wonder what turned me into such a coward, what triggered my impaired mental faculties
I wonder why Mum has always said I have a good heart
I can't feel my heart
It's a muscle, a pump
A heart is blood and meat
Fuck it
Fuck the heart
A voice tells me everything is going to get better
It speaks to me from outer space
The voice tells me to listen to my gut instinct
I'm constantly working against my gut instinct
Fuck gut instincts
No

Yes
There's only white here
And whenever I turn around, it's like a red déjà vu
Red
Red's been here
Now I remember
I lay in his lap and wept and he told me he'd always love me
He asked for my forgiveness
We signed divorce papers
I've got a Mastercard bill for more than 30,000 kroner
I don't know how I'm going to be able to look anyone in the eye
Whenever I do, it feels as if they're sucking the life out of me
Like they're eating me up
Like they're exposing me
I've got no friends
Lisa is my only friend
Lisa's not here
Lisa will never be here again
Lisa is a bomb that has detonated, just like me
I've pissed all over my chances in life
Haha
I've taken a great big shit all over my destiny
Haha
I'm waiting for a helping hand
I need someone to help me

I need someone to save me
I can't do it by myself
I've got impaired mental faculties
Mum calls to tell me that one of my childhood friends
has killed herself
I admire her
I wish I were that brave
I know that there's more out there
I know that
I listen carefully
I know I need to listen to the voice from outer space
The other voices, they aren't mine
This is my voice
The voice from outer space is trying to save me

10

I feel cleansed
I pack up my things on the ward and feel ready to start afresh
I feel so tired of all of this
I've written a wish list for life
I've gotten closer to the voice from outer space
We talk in secret
The doctors tell me it's important not to engage with the voice
They think it's gone
They think I'm taking my medication and that's why I'm better
I'm not taking any medication, but I do feel better
I know best, and they've proven that they haven't got a clue
I go back to my flat
It's dark and squalid
I give notice

Throw away everything apart from my teddy bears and
a few CDs, books and items of clothing
I pack a rucksack with everything I need
I'm standing out on the street
The letter from Jorg is still in my bag
I sit down on a bench
Clutch the envelope in both hands
It's crumpled
The glue on the flap has lost its stickiness
I light a cigarette
Work my way through a packet
The envelope is damp with sweat
When I've taken my final drag of the last of the
cigarettes, I open the envelope
My temples throb
I close my eyes as I unfold the letter
It's been handwritten on lined paper
Boyish handwriting
Joined up letters

Sometimes I can speak to you in my dreams
Sometimes I dream about dogs for weeks at a time
I'm scared
Life is short when it comes down to it
It's hard for me to accept that nothing lasts forever
Our choices and actions are consequences of a pursuit of love
It's all that anyone wants, it's all that we need
Sooner or later I'm going to lose everything, myself included

I think I choose hate in order to protect myself
I think I push myself closer to the edge in order to protect myself
I think chasing the high is a form of love

Or
I don't know
I don't know if any hope remains
I don't know if all hope is lost
I just don't know

I think
the greatest of these is love
I think
we're all filled with the holy spirit.

J

I think about the holy spirit
The holy spirit and the voice from outer space
It's as if something is nodding inside me, inside my stomach
An intense force flaring up
It's incredible
I drink too much
It feels pointless but I do it anyway
It's a salute to the holy spirit and the fact that the voice from outer space isn't actually from outer space, but from my stomach
I wander around the city
I wish I could find Red and tell him everything
My mobile is locked
I try calling him from a payphone
He doesn't pick up
I go to a grunge bar near Karl Johans gate where he used to hang out
Sit at one of the tables outside
Doodle on my plaster cast
Heart after heart after heart
It's like I'm in love with myself
Except that it's not a crazy kind of love
It feels real
Full and round and flowing
Like flames and fireworks all at once
I drink a lot
The beer has no effect on who I am

It just strengthens my perception of the holy spirit
Of myself
I raise a glass to the feelings that have never flourished
within me before now
I read my notebook filled with my own awful poetry
Bad poetry annoys me
Bad poetry ought never to see the light of day
I tear out the pages and eat them one by one
Perhaps if I'm able to physically digest them they'll
assume a new poetic form, I think to myself
Like some kind of process of metamorphosis
I wash them down with beer
I realise that I'm just going to end up shitting paper
I stop eating the poems and burn them in the ashtray
instead
Cremate them one-by-one
Haha
It's warm and sunny
It smells like summer
People smell of sweat and sun cream
I love the smell of sweat and sun cream
I love people, the fact that everyone has the opportunity
to be here today
I laugh out loud at myself
Then I write in my notebook so it looks as if I've just
come up with something clever
People glance over at my table

They must be curious to know what I'm writing, I think to myself
I can understand that
I nod to the people at the next table
I can feel myself getting closer to the point of losing it
I can sense that I need to take it down a notch or two
Suddenly I can see myself from the outside
Suddenly I'm able to analyse my actions
It's sick
It's unnerving
It comes with a sense of responsibility
I don't know how I feel about it
I decide to forget about it and carry on with what I was doing before
I try losing it
It's just not the same
A sensc of reason builds up inside me
I freak out
Order a shot a Fernet, two beers and two espressos
Down the espressos and wash them down with the Fernet
Scrawl hurriedly in my book
It's my gut instincts
I write, 'Fuck you, gut instincts, fuck you!'
I feel guilty, like I'm betraying an old friend
I scribble an apology

I tell my gut that we can talk tomorrow, but that today
I'm going to get wasted and do weird, irrational things
I ask it to work with me, just for tonight
The sense of reason starts to disappear
I heave a sigh of relief and write thanks, then doodle a smiley face in my notebook
Then a heart
I think about the fact that I've just engaged in a discussion with my own feelings
I'm on a high
I'm in control

I look at all of the tables
Scrutinise the people around them
Make up stories about what they're doing
Jorg is sitting in the corner
He's at a table with a girl
I feel like I'm tripping
It's unbelievable
Fucking unreal
I do a few basic reality checks
Yep
That's Jorg alright, and it looks as if he's on a date
He's laughing at the girl's jokes
I feel jealous
She has a ring in her nose and piercings all over her face

It makes me furious, people are all such posers nowadays
Everybody feels the need to have their own fucking style
I couldn't give a shit about any of that
I want people to misinterpret me
I want them to form their own misguided judgements
I get up
Everything goes black
I trip over a chair
Pick it up and put it back in its place
I hurry over to the table where Jorg and the poser are sitting
'WHO THE FUCK DO WE HAVE HERE, THEN?!' I bellow in his ear
He turns around
I'm dying
He smiles and leaps up, spills beer all over the girl with the face full of metal
He hugs me long and hard as she mops up beer with a few flimsy napkins
We shout
Talk over one another
The girl looks uneasy
Jorg kisses my cheeks and hugs me tight over and over again
I never want him to let me go
I want to tell his date that she's no longer needed

She's played her part
Instead he introduces us
Her name is Karianne
She compliments my name
I win
I ask if I can take a seat, a rhetorical question
I ignore her stammers and buy us a round before fetching myself a chair
I'm in my element
I rattle on
Blethering at a mile a minute
Karianne doesn't say much
Jorg laughs at everything that comes out of my mouth
Eventually Karianne says she has to be at work early the next day
She hugs Jorg
'So, you'll call me?' she says
'Sure, sure,' Jorg tells her, turning away as he says the words
I tell him everything
Tell him I only opened his letter today, that I really do think we're soulmates, really truly
Jorg agrees
We both think that the fact we met here by chance like this, today of all days, is all the proof we could ever need
We talk about the holy spirit and the fact that love is the highest power

We raise our glasses to something new every few minutes, huddling close in one long embrace
This is the best day of my life
When the bar closes, we roam the streets, shouting and brawling
Jorg tells me he spent a long time feeling angry with me
I tell him that's OK, that I never stop feeling angry at myself
We throw ourselves at one another, hugging and kissing until our skin bruises
We roll around on the asphalt
The morning sun comes up
I'm filled to the brim
I breathe
Deep breaths that fill my belly
We come across some scaffolding and have sex under the tarpaulin
We laugh at the idea of being arrested for having sex in public
I don't know how this is going to end
I can't think how something so good could possibly end well
I feel sad and collapse down onto the kerb
Jorg puts his arm around me
He's crying too
He has no idea how everything is going to end either, he says

We agree to worry about that later and return to the tarpaulin to have sex

I live out of my rucksack at Jorg's place
I'm scared
Happy, too
Things are good and scary and strange
I experience things I've never experienced before
So many feelings course through me
I've stirred an unfamiliar sensation
I'm not as naïve as I used to be
It's painful
I have to do something with everything that I feel
I almost wish that none of this new stuff had ever happened, wish that everything was just how it used to be
That the voice inside me was just a symptom of my psychosis
I take the subway up to the ward and sit outside
I long to be inside
I realise I can never go back
It feels like I've moved away from home all over again
I seek out the madness
Seeking and seeking but never finding anything
Madness has turned to logic
Even when I'm shaking and thinking of nothing but death, logic reigns triumphant
My gut instincts tell me everything is going to be OK
That I'm in control
Even smoking feels pointless
Every kind of high feels pointless

I miss the days when getting high was crucial in keeping
me from falling apart
I want to be dependent
To run myself into the ground
I gaze in at the ward lounge through the window
A patient is playing chess with a nurse
I knock
They can't hear me
I want to play chess with the nurse too
I want a cheese sandwich and a glass of milk and a cup
of coffee
I want it NOW
I leave
This is ridiculous, my gut tells me
'You're acting like a child.'
I go home to Jorg
I ask him if he feels like a child
He tells me he does
I ask him if he has gut instincts
He tells me yes, they're always bothering him
I ask him if he suppresses them, if they leave him alone
if he just ignores them for long enough
He tells me that hasn't worked up until now
unfortunately, but that it might be our gut instincts
that saves us when it comes to the crunch
He hugs me and tells me that he's fond of them, really
That they keep him from death, stop him from turning
to heroin

Jorg tells me he once drank tea made from a jungle plant
The plant contains the same stuff that's released in the brain when we die
I ask him what happened
He tells me he came face-to-face with his demons and an angelic creature that watched over him
He thinks it might have been his gut instincts, he tells me, or perhaps the holy spirit
I ask him if he's talking about Jesus
He laughs and tells me no, not Jesus, but maybe whatever Jesus was in touch with with back in his day
I ask him if he's talking about God
He tells me it could be viewed that way, of course, but that he thinks it's something else, something different
Something deep within us, something good, something intended to help us
I ask him if he has any of the jungle plant he can give to me
He tells me I'll have to travel to Peru and get a hold of some for myself
He knows a shaman out there
I'm pleased
I ask him if he wants to come with me
He tells me he'd like to, but this is something I have to do for myself
I make up my mind to go to Peru

Jorg says I'll have to be ready
I ask him when I'll be ready
He tells me I'll know when it's time
I fall asleep in his lap

There are times I think Jorg and I are more than lovers
I don't actually believe that Jorg and I are lovers, not really
I feel like we share a bond of blood
We often have to stop when we're having sex because it feels too incestuous
Perhaps we were brother and sister in another life
Perhaps we're on the same path in life, or however else you might put it

Mum has invited me over for Sunday lunch
I'm dreading it
I take the tram
I'm reluctant
I feel nervous
My brother and sister are going to be there too
I haven't seen them in ages
Mum hands me a glass of wine
I neck it in one
I drink three glasses before the meal is over
I'm drunk
A strange mood takes over
I feel guilty
I drink even more to make myself feel better
My mood improves and I insist on singing

I can't remember the lyrics and start to cry
My brother and sister go up to their rooms to play on their PlayStations
I follow them upstairs and tell them they need to open their eyes and look out of their windows instead of hiding indoors playing video games
They laugh at the fact I call them video games
They ask if I was born in 1950 or something
I slam the door and realise that I'm not in any position to lecture them on anything
Mum tells me I've had enough wine for now
I agree with her but carry on drinking anyway
I divert her attention by asking if she's read anything good lately
She tells me I'm welcome to borrow whatever I like the look of before picking out a trashy crime novel
I make it very clear that I never read crime novels, under any circumstances
I scan the bookshelves
In front of me is a green book
The author's name is Eva
I pull it out and open it at the first page
There's a picture of Eva
It says that she's 83, comes from Bergen and works as a psychologist

I'm moving down a tunnel
I can see a light at the end
Green as far as the eye can see
A horse is waiting there
It's grey and white
I can hear it speaking to me via my thoughts
It tells me that it's mine and I can ride it whenever I want
I can't face the thought of moving
The horse lowers its head and lifts me up onto its back
My body is rigid, I feel paralysed
I tumble to the ground
The horse bends down and picks me up once again
I sit on its back
The horse and I are one
We ride off into the distance
I guide it with my mind
We arrive in a dark city
Barcelona
I've never been before
The horse stops outside a door
I step over the threshold and into the room
It's large and empty
A woman is sitting on a chair in the middle of the room
She's old and slightly plump
She tells me her name is Eva and she's from Bergen
I ask her where she is now

She tells me I can come to her when I'm ready, that she'll help me
She laughs out loud and the sound reverberates around us
I ask where I can find her
She laughs again
She points at my stomach

I wake up drenched in sweat to the sound of Mum's voice
A gentle, lovely voice, one I haven't heard in years
I tell her about my dream
She's overcome
Tells me she knew I'd find a way out, that she's spoken to a psychic who told her there are forces in the universe watching over me
We can't go losing our heads over this, I tell her
We look up Eva online and I send her an email
I ask her if she has time to see me
I tell her I've been declared insane but life on medication isn't working for me
I tell her I've stopped taking my pills
I write that I'm still not well, that it's making day-to-day life difficult

That I often do things I regret, and that there's some sort of membrane between what I want to do and whatever I end up doing
That I really want to be an actor, but that it's a dream that seems all too distant for the time being
I tell her I use and abuse alcohol and drugs, and that I've got a death wish that sometimes becomes difficult to ignore
That I don't know who I am
That I change my mind as frequently as I change my socks
That I'm horrible to the people around me
That my sex life is depraved
I ring Eva's doorbell
I'm nervous
She buzzes me in and I take the lift up to her floor
It feels like I'm on my way to parents' evening
A short, plump lady opens the door
'Well then,' she says in a thick Bergen accent, 'you'd best come on in.'
She tells me to take off my shoes
I consider turning around and leaving then and there
It smells old inside, and there's art on the walls
She's got a cigar in one hand
I follow her into the living room and she gestures for me to take a seat
There's an awkward silence

She tells me she has a lot on her plate and I'll need to spit it out
I tell her a bit about my life, about everything that's gone wrong up until now
She tells me she's sorry to hear it
That she's glad I'm out of psychiatric care, that it's the very essence of madness itself
Eva tells me that she was once mad as a hatter herself
She gazes at me long and hard
I wish that I could disappear in a puff of smoke, I feel tiny and delicate
I look down and start to cry
She tells me I look as if I'm feeling a bit too sorry for myself, if she's frank
I'm a beautiful young woman, she says, but it's no good if I refuse to take responsibility for my actions and the fact I've got the wrong attitude
She tells me that it seems like I feel that the world owes me something
I realise deep inside that everything she's saying is true
I want to leave
I tell her I think she's a bitter, fat, lonely old bag
She tells me there's obviously nothing ailing my spirit, which is a good thing
She tells me that hope is in sight, that I'll be a new person before too long
I ask her how she knows that

She tells me that she doesn't know it, but that she
believes in me
She sees herself in me
My anger is a driving force, she says, and I should
protect that
Eva points at her midriff

'In here is something I call My Inner Self. It's a good thing; it knows everything and it can do anything. My Inner Self knows best, it's a friend, a guide. You might find yourself overwhelmed with love when you establish contact with Your Inner Self. It might feel like God's love, but you have to promise me that you'll never believe that it's God, never, under any circumstances. God does not exist. God was created by humanity because humanity can't face the fact that we're all going to die, to disappear from the earth one day. Your Inner Self is you and you alone. Your Inner Self is the sense of rationality that lives within you. All it asks is that you trust in It. Trust It without hesitation. Let go and trust. It's you. Nothing that exists inside you can do you any harm.'

She narrows her eyes
They're like two fine lines in her face
She smiles, looks over at me
Tears are running down my cheeks
She looks like an owl, or a tree

She asks me why I'm crying
I tell her I don't know, but that what she said was so lovely
I tell her I think I discovered My Inner Self a few weeks ago
That I call it my gut instinct
She tells me that's fantastic and I'm already well on my way
Now all that's left to do is to trust in it
She tells me it's important not to be afraid, not to obstruct it
Not to fear the changes that are about to occur
She tells me it might mean a few years of work
That there's a lot of restructuring to be done inside me
That my perception of reality is set to undergo a brutal shift
(UGH
UGH UGH UGH
UGH
ALL THIS MAKES ME SICK
FUCK OFF
FUCK YOU
I'LL NEVER FIND MY FUCKING INNER SELF
I'LL KILL THE PAIR OF US BEFORE I DO
DO YOU REALLY BELIEVE IN ANY OF THIS SHIT?
I'M EMBARRASSED
GET ME OUT OF HERE

FUCK OFFFFFFF)
I tell Eva that something inside me is putting up a fight, that I'm sensing opposition
She tells me that's not so unusual
There's bound to be something inside fighting to keep its place
My negative side is used to getting its own way
(NOOOOOO DON'T LISTEN TO THE OLD CRONE)
Eva tells me to pay her whatever I can afford
I tell her I can afford to pay her one hundred kroner per session, and we agree on that
(ARE YOU REALLY GOING TO PAY TO LISTEN TO THAT SHIT? FUCK OFF I'LL BLOW MY BRAINS OUT BEFORE OUR NEXT SESSION)
I have two voices now
My Inner Self and My Angry Self
My Angry Self is much angrier than it used to be
It grows angrier and angrier with every passing day, and it doesn't feel like the most natural part of me anymore, more like a fragment on the sidelines, screaming at all hours
It's only grown worse since I sidelined it
My Angry Self doesn't like anyone
Or anything
My Angry Self wants to murder anyone and everyone, to drag the world into misery
It wants others to suffer

My Inner Self is calm
It has perspective and insight, it's tolerant and longs for everyone to thrive
My Inner Self is fond of me, it pities My Angry Self
I've always rooted for the villains
I like My Angry Self
My Inner Self rubs me up the wrong way
It's so fucking sanctimonious
I don't think I'm ready to take it seriously
I tell My Angry Self I'll hear it out too
It needn't worry about being forgotten
That calms it down

My new psyche is difficult to relate to
It's not just My Angry Self in there
There are others now, too:
The Child
The Misanthrope
The Saboteur and
The Super

The Super is my favourite
Lots gets done when The Super is around
I'm happy and cool and confident
The Super is manic, filled with energy
It loves attention and feels positive about life
The Child is afraid and can't face anything
All it wants is to be cuddled and mollycoddled
The Misanthrope is clever
Cleverer than My Angry Self
It makes sound arguments that are hard to counter and is superior in every way
The Saboteur is demanding
Like a Trojan horse, it strikes when I least expect it
It obviously wants to ensure that nothing ever goes to plan
It shuns every chance at success
I suspect it had a part to play in my audition
Eva and I talk about these additions to my psyche
She laughs and tells me they're all a part of me, that each of them feels stifled

She tells me it's up to me to decide if they have any
sway over me
I tell her I don't think that's the case, that they do their
own thing regardless of what I have to say
She takes a firm tone with me
Tells me I need to listen up
Tells me I have a tendency to play the victim
It's high time I listen to those around me who are older,
those with a bit more experience, she says
I need to take back control, she tells me
Her tone becomes gentler and she smiles with
narrowed eyes
I ask her if it's anything like a football match
She tells me yes, it is kind of like a football match

When I'm with Eva, a lot of what's inside me is in order
There are no unwelcome guests
It's like they've recognised that when I'm with her
there's no point in them even trying
Eva knows what to expect

I feel whole in her company
Eva tells me it's because I'm in touch with My Inner Self
She tells me I'm making good progress, too
I tell her I feel like I've still got a long way to go
She says she thinks so too, but it might not be as great a distance as I think

I've always rooted for the villains
I don't want to disappoint them
Villains need champions too
Now it's onwards and upwards or nothing at all
Now it's onwards and upwards
Or

I've made up my mind that I'm going to Peru
I've spent my benefits on a ticket
Jorg tells me he's busy with life here and that I just have to go for it
He tells me he might come and visit me in a while
I don't know how long I'll be away for
It's a strange feeling
I might just disappear at the periphery
I haven't told Eva that I'll be gone for a long while
I'm scared she might talk me out of it
I feel uneasy when I think about the fact that Eva might advise me against my trip
Mum thinks I'm going out there to work with orphans
She's proud and happy
Now life can really begin, she says
Now life can really begin

I fly out to Peru
Drink whisky on the flight
I'm gripped by a fear of flying
I've never been afraid of it before
I get so drunk that they refuse to serve me anymore
I brace myself against the man in the seat next to me
It makes him feel uncomfortable
I've nowhere to go when I arrive
I want to jump out of the plane
I scratch at myself

It feels like I've got lice
I tug at the air hostess' arm, beg her to check my scalp
She hands me a glass of water
I throw it at a child
The child bursts into tears
I wonder what made me do what I just did
I grab the crotch of the man sitting next to me
I wonder why
I don't recognise these actions or reactions as my own
I try saying my name out loud
It sounds foreign and strange
I talk to My Inner Self
I've lost contact
I can't seem to reach it, can't seem to reach anything inside me
I don't recognise myself
Can't feel anything but panic
It rises up from a primitive space deep inside
I regret leaving
From this point onwards, I'm primitive
From this point onwards, the primitive is what counts
Perhaps it can save me
Perhaps the primitive is what really counts

FUCK
Help
OK
But, but
Hahahaaaa
Eeep
Piss myself
No matter
Plane lands
Plane shakes
Roaring
Scared
Approach car
Climb in
Taxi?
Taxi
Drive
Hotel
Bed
Sleep
Wake
Beer
Beer no good
Scared
Alone
Alone for first time ever
Left luggage at airport
Lie in bed three days

Dizzy
Wrong decision
Or is it
Sleep
Look out window
Hard to see
Car
Step outside
Believe in God now
Alone
God is my daddy
Go to church
Talk to priest
Priest doesn't speak English
Leave
Talk to people about God
Dios Mio!
Go to hell
Buy cocaine from a man
Fun times
Fun for me
Cocaine every half hour
Watch out for police, says the man
The boys in blue
Hey!
Dip finger in cocaine, shove finger up nose
Forget the time
Ten minutes

Coca tea
Tedious coca tea
A lady grabs me, wants money
Baby on hip
Poor thing
Hand her cocaine
Buy more for me
Meet some Swedish guys
Swedish guys laugh
Funny old me
Masses of cocaine
Sex in hotel
All together now
On holiday
Cocaine in my cunt
Party time
Take it in turns
Look in mirror
Who's that there?
Break mirror
Haha
Nothing stops
Bleeding hand
Lick blood
Blood on boys
Funny
Laugh
Cocaine

Back inside
Hurts a bit
Dry
Rough when they do it over and over
Throw up
Tied tight
Cocaine in mouth and up nose and all over cock
Cock in cunt and in mouth
Cock up arse
Not good
Bleeding
Body shaking because masses of cocaine
Cocaine
Almost pass out
Cocaine
Shaking
Cock
Cocaine
Blood
Water
Cum
Cocaine
Take a break from cock and cocaine
Boys do acid
Acid on tongue
Tired now
Can't carry on
But

On holiday
Boys laid back
Me laid back
Colours on ceiling
Nice, that
On and on
Boring
Lady at door
Looks nasty
Old lady
Eva?
Angry at me
Screams in face
Scared now
Scream at lady
Lady wants to kill
Pick up glass
Stab lady
Maggots spill out of belly
Maggots fill up mouth
Boys pull weird faces
They not happy now
Tie wrists
Me not happy now
Scared
Not fun
Nightmare for me
Too late

Never the same again
Never the same again
Never the same again
Never the same again
Life ruined
Cry
Life ruined
Pull plug
No connection
Grab belt
Buckled tight
Boy on phone
Kick boy in face
Boy punches
Pulls out cock
Numb now
Cocaine
Cocaine for everyone
Boys touch cocks
Cocks black
They be negroes, I shout
Boys angry
Fists in face
I'm sorry
Laugh
Fun, this
Fun in the sun

I wake up in the jungle
Hands tied behind my back
Body and cunt aching
A gang of boys approaches
They look Peruvian
They're not Swedish, at any rate
They're speaking Spanish
They're speaking loudly
There's a bandana over my mouth
I try to speak
They kick me in the face
They look at me like I'm their prey
Like an animal
No matter
I'm primitive
More primitive than them
I wait for my instincts to kick in
Out here it's dog eat dog
I realise things aren't looking good
But anything can happen out here in the natural world
I lie still and close my eyes
They drag me up and into a car
I can see one of the Swedes
He's taking money
Payment
For me
They're paying for me
He's going to die

He's going to die
I'll kill him
I will
But maybe I won't need to
The indian kills him for me
Shoots him in the head
I laugh
I take back what I said about indians
Indians don't wear polo shirts and shorts
Indians have feathers in their hair and walk around
    naked or near enough
I'll show you an indian, I think to myself
When I'm cut loose I'll become an indian for real
I'll live out here in the jungle
I'll fuck another indian, we'll start a whole fucking tribe
FUCK
The fake indian is coming my way
I don't look him in the eye
It's important to play it cool
He leans over
I look right at him
Try to show him I'm on his side
That I'm primitive, just like him
It works
He loosens the belt
I'm free
Only the jungle can save me now

The indian with the belt is called Pablo
I call him Pablo Picasso
We're friends now
He has a friend called Paco
I call him Taco
He likes that
They like me
They have a hut in the jungle
We live there together
We're companions now
They teach me Spanish
They teach me how the jungle works, how to protect myself against dangerous influences
Everything is a dangerous influence in principle
They show me the jungle plant
Teach me to deal drugs and steal trucks
I'm not scared anymore
I'm not scared of anything anymore
Pablo and Paco tell me that they're not going to hurt me
That they protect anything they consider their territory
They consider me their territory
I feel happy and safe when they say that
This is the kind of loyalty I need
I feel loyal to them
We make a pact
We boil the jungle plant and drink it
The effects are insane

I run wild and lie down and roll around and cry
I talk to the plants
I find a tree, it's my grandmother, just like in
Pocahontas
I tie palm leaves together with jungle vines and wear
them instead of clothing
I'm Pocahontas
I'm filthy
I'm filthy and free

I live from hand to mouth
Well, from the hands of others, to be more precise
I take what isn't mine, get high, wreak havoc and brawl
I hold a gun for the first time
I hold it to a man's head
He's terrified
Tingling in my stomach
It leaves me exhilarated
I take whatever I want
Every man and woman for him and herself
The law of the jungle
The pack is all that matters
My pack is perfect
Strongest and handsomest and most ruthless of them
all

I'm the ace up their sleeve, Paco and Pablo say
People trust me, they're charmed by me
When we need to get out of trouble, my body is our
    weapon of choice
There's nothing you can't fuck your way out of in Peru
The police are some of our most loyal customers
I think I've fucked my way through the entire squad
It's so easy
I get a gun of my own
A huge, heavy black thing
It feels almost like when I got my first Barbie doll
I cover it in stickers
A pink skull, a heart and a flower
I wander around with Pablo and Paco
We take cocaine and smoke marijuana every day
This is the life
I'm not even scared of insects anymore
I wake up one day with a huge spider on my leg
Spiders are my new spirit animal
I feel content
There's nothing I miss
Well, nothing apart from Jorg, maybe
I might miss Jorg a little bit
But that doesn't matter
I think he'd be proud of me

We ride into town on our mopeds
Loot a shop
I shoot a man for the first time
The man behind the counter
He won't hand over the cash
I shoot him in the stomach
I'm a bad shot
Don't know what to say
Pablo and Paco can't believe their eyes
We weren't supposed to shoot anyone
They shout at me
I'm scared
They check to see if he's alive
He's alive
I'm sweating
Sweating and shaking
They drag me out of the shop and onto the back of a moped
We ride back into the jungle
They lay me down on the bed
I'm shaking like a leaf
Pablo and Paco are talking loudly
The tiny vibrations slice at my flesh
I have to wake up, they tell me
They slap my face
Feel my forehead
I've got a fever, they say

They give me something green to drink
I knock it back
Call them wannabe indians
They laugh
Tell me they're real-life indians, that it's me who's the wannabe
And they're right
They talk on the phone
Shout at some guy
Point at me
They're talking fast now
Talking in Spanish
I can't work out what they're saying
I throw up
Throw up for two hours straight
There are snakes in my bed
A heaving throng
P and P hold me down
I'm hallucinating, they tell me
I don't believe them
I don't believe them
This is real
Snakes slither from my belly
They slither all around me, slipping into my eye sockets and between my thighs and up inside me
Paco washes my body
The snakes disappear
A bright light blinds me

A light from above
This is the day I die, I think to myself
But I don't die
A woman arrives
She mumbles in a language I can't understand
Calm and quick
I ask what she wants from me
She tells me she's here to cleanse me, speaks to me in
Norwegian
She's Norwegian all of a sudden
I ask her how she got here
She tells me she has no concept of time or space
She's from Kristiansand, she says
Well then, I tell her, cleanse me and be done
I ask her if the effects will last forever
Nothing lasts forever, she says
It's the worst thing she could have said
I realise I'm going to die, that everyone I know is going
to die
I sob in her lap
I sob for hours
She strokes my hair
'Everything is going to be alright,' she sings
'Everything is going to be alright'
That's a lie though
Nothing is going to be alright
Nothing can ever be alright again
I shot a man

I look up
He's sitting right there, the man I shot
A hole in his stomach
His eyes black
He strokes my hair
Wraps his hands around my neck
Grasps my head
Twists it
Snap
My head is no longer attached to my body
I scream
I scream with every fibre of my being
My skin screams
My hair screams
Enough now
Enough now
I want out
OUT
Help me out
Where can I go
Without my head
Having a heart is pointless if you're headless
There's not a bad bone in me, I say
I'm not a bad person, not really
I'm sorry about what happened
Can't you put my head back
Please
I promise never to shoot anyone ever again

Honest
The man is gone
I check
My head is back where it should be
I look for Pablo and Paco
They're not here
The hut is bare
I'm all alone
There's not even a bed
I'm lying on the floor
I get up to go to the door
There's no door here
There's no door
No window
Not a single pipe
No way in or way out
I bang on the wall
I can forget that
It's made of brick
But this is a treehouse, I shout
'This wall is made of wood, anyone can see that!'
No reply
I hear the echo of my own voice
I scour every nook and cranny
I find a mirror
I look into it
It's empty
I can't see myself

I have no reflection
I close my eyes and count to ten
When I open them again, there's a reflection there
It's my sister
I smash the mirror
It won't smash, but it disappears
I smash through the wall
I can step through the wall
I step outside
I'm outside
YES
I find a well
I pull on the rope to lift the bucket, but there is no
bucket
I pull and pull and pull
Pull for hours
Eventually something emerges
I've got something
It's a book
I read the cover
Necessity is the Mother of Invention, by Eva
The sight of it makes me furious
I toss it back down into the well
Pull on the rope again
Catch hold of something else
A sock
A child's sock
A sock with a non-slip rubber sole

A child's gym sock
My gym sock
I wore this sock back when I was seven, eight years old, maybe
I put it in my pocket
Pull
I pull up a Norwegian flag and a picture of Leonardo
I stop to look at the picture
It hurts to look him in the eye
I've let him down
I'm such a let-down
What am I supposed to do now
I've got nowhere to go
I place the picture and the flag on the ground
I have to keep pulling
Pull
This'll be the last time I pull anything up from inside this well, I tell myself
Pull
Pull
Pull
It's a cassette tape
A cassette tape
Nobody uses cassette tapes anymore
Where am I supposed to get my hands on a cassette player?
Could it be that I need to pull one more time?
I take a gamble

Sure enough, it pays off
A cassette player
I pop the tape into the player
Press play
Hear Mum's soothing voice
She's talking to me
I'm four years old
She asks me to sing a song I've made up
It's about wigs and trees
It's a funny one
I sound so sweet that it brings me to tears
Floods of tears
I sing one more song
A song about an owl
An owl father and an owl mother
It's another funny one
And that's when it hits me
The love in Mum's voice
The tenderness
As if she were talking to something that might break if she were to say the wrong thing
Her absolute, total, unconditional acceptance of me

She sounds so pretty
I feel the warmth that flows from her, warmth that flows all the way from Norway
I feel her hope, her faith
Hope and faith in the fact that I'm going to be OK
That I'm going to be just fine
Happy
Kind to others
Kind to myself
Have children of my own
Love them the way that she's loved me
Give them a cassette tape of their own for singing songs about animals and making up jokes
Let them be dippy and daft
Tell them how wonderful they are, no matter what
Laugh at their silly jokes
Bathe them
Blow bubbles together
Let them eat their fill of ice cream on special occasions
Tuck them up in bed when they're all worn out on Christmas Eve
These are the gifts that Mum gave to me

ZE
RO

Gave to me in the hope that I'd pass them onto another
Mum is a hero
Mum
I love you

I wake to a bang
Then another
Gasp for air
Open my eyes
Pablo is lying on top of me, his brain spattered all over the wall, all over me
Paco is propped up in the corner, a gaping hole in his body
His tongue lolls out of his mouth
There's a gun to my head
Shouting
Words
Irrelevant
Clasped hands
Closed eyes
Squeezed tight
Leonardo
Jorg
Red

1

2

3

4

5

6

7

8

9

10

Peep
Black
Peep
Black
Black in my head
But tell me
Where am I, sir?
I knew it
Jab
Jab my finger in a hole
Full of holes
Wet holes
Bloody
Sounds like a cunt
Suck on that
Ha
Home to the old country
Finally
NO
Can't escape
Can't escape the jungle
The jungle is all around

I'm lying in a bed
There's a space beside me
Empty space
Nobody's space
My space
I'm lying in a bed
Jorg is beside me
Jorg looks at me and pats my head
Jorg tells me that if nothing else, it's time we acknowledged that it's now or never
I tell him it is now or never
That I've been saying that all along
Everything
Every moment
Now or never
I tell him there's a monster inside me
He tells me there's a monster inside everyone
It's just a question of letting it out once in a while, he says
Treating it like a guard dog
A guard dog
I'm lying in a bed

Eva is lying beside me
Eva smiles at me, her eyes narrowed, tells me that I'm a crazy little girl
Eva tells me that was one cool trip
That depends on how you look at it, I say
Eva lights a cigar, lies back, smiles up at the ceiling
I tell her there's a monster inside me
Eva chuckles and blows smoke rings into the air
That's nothing to worry about, she tells me
I've already solved that problem, she says
She sounds stern
We've already spoken about this, she says
It's not a real monster, she says
Just something I've left behind, something I've abandoned
Eva tells me to get well soon and to call on her one of these days

I'm standing on stage
There's a spotlight on me and me alone
I'm beautiful, gifted, an all-round talent
I'm standing on stage
There's a spotlight on me and me alone
I'm holding a broken violin in one hand
I play
The violin plays notes the likes of which no man has ever heard before
Warped and weird and beautiful notes that make no sense at all
People ask where I discovered the notes
I tell them I found them in the jungle